MW00846586

PEARL KILLIFISHES
THE CYNOLEBIATINAE
Systematics and Biogeography of the
Neotropical Annual Fish Subfamily
(Cyprinodontiformes: Rivulidae)

Cynolebias whitei. Photo by Wolfgang Sommer.

by
Wilson J. E. M. Costa

Distributed in the UNITED STATES to the Pet Trade by T.F.H. Publications, Inc., One T.F.H. Plaza, Neptune City, NJ 07753; distributed in the UNITED STATES to the Bookstore and Library Trade by National Book Network, Inc. 4720 Boston Way, Lanham MD 20706; in CANADA to the Pet Trade by H & L Pet Supplies Inc., 27 Kingston Crescent, Kitchener, Ontario N2B 2T6; Rolf C. Hagen Ltd., 3225 Sartelon Street, Montreal 382 Quebec; in CANADA to the Book Trade by Vanwell Publishing Ltd., 1 Northrup Crescent, St. Catharines, Ontario L2M 6P5 ; in ENGLAND by T.F.H. Publications, PO Box 15, Waterlooville PO7 6BQ; in AUSTRALIA AND THE SOUTH PACIFIC by T.F.H. (Australia), Pty. Ltd., Box 149, Brookvale 2100 N.S.W., Australia; in NEW ZEALAND by Brooklands Aquarium Ltd. 5 McGiven Drive, New Plymouth, RD1 New Zealand; in Japan by T.F.H. Publications, Japan—Jiro Tsuda, 10-12-3 Ohjidai, Sakura, Chiba 285, Japan; in SOUTH AFRICA by Lopis (Pty) Ltd., P.O. Box 39127, Booysens, 2016, Johannesburg, South Africa. Published by T.F.H. Publications, Inc.
MANUFACTURED IN THE UNITED STATES OF AMERICA
BY T.F.H. PUBLICATIONS, INC.

CONTENTS

ACKNOWLEDGMENTS

I am indebted to several people who have accompanied me into the field during these last ten years of studies on cynolebiatine fishes, in particular to Cláudia Bove, Gilberto Brasil, João Alves, Kenny Tanizaki, and Margareth Melgaço.

For loans or donations of specimens I thank Carlos Cruz, Décio Moraes, Francisco Mago-Leccia, Frank Almoeder, Gilberto Brasil, Heraldo Britski, India Moreira, Júlio Ghisolfi, Lynne Parenti, Marcelo Notare, Osvaldo Oyakawa, Raul Vaz-Ferreira, and Robert R. Miller.

I am grateful for the support provided at Universidade Federal do Rio de Janeiro by Sérgio Annibal, and at Museu de Zoologia da Universidade de São Paulo by Naércio Menezes, Heraldo Britski, and José Figueiredo.

Gilberto Brasil provided me with valuable collecting data and photos of fishes and fish habitats.

I extend warm thanks to Cláudia Bove for her friendship, assistance, and support in the last stages of this study.

Eliane Vicente and Margareth Melgaço provided me with substantial laboratory assistance.

Nelson Papavero, Dalton Amorim, and Sandro Bonato reinforced my enthusiasm to study the phylogenetic relationships of rivulids.

Financial support was given by Fundação de Amparo á Pesquisa do Estado de São Paulo (grant during doctoral studies, 1985-1987), Fundação de Amparo á Pesquisa do Estado do Rio de Janeiro (collecting trip to Espírito Santo and Bahia, 1990), and Conselho Nacional de Pesquisas (collecting trip to Mato Grosso do Sul, 1991).

The manuscript was benefited from the valuable criticisms of Maurice Kottelat.

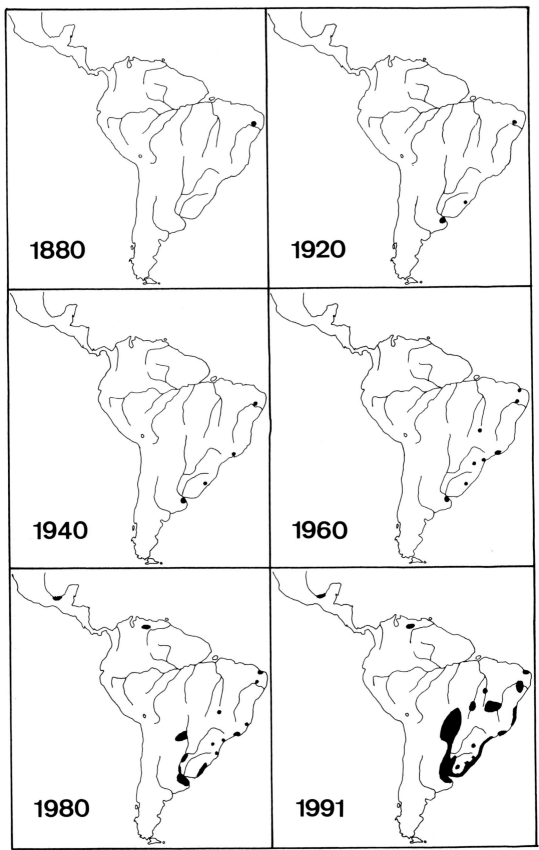

Fig. 1. Known range of fishes of the subfamily Cynolebiatinae at six different years between 1880 and 1991.

INTRODUCTION

Cynolebiatine fishes are members of the Neotropical freshwater ichthyofauna, which is the most diversified in the world. This ichthyofauna includes an estimated 7,000 species, many of which are still undescribed. They mainly belong to the orders Characiformes, Siluriformes, and Cyprinodontiformes, comprising a complex of endemic and monophyletic assemblages.

Scientific expeditions prior to the late nineteenth century dealt almost exclusively with the larger species. But Neotropical fish families are also well represented by small species, and it is only recently that they started to become known. Therefore, besides being the most numerous in species, the fishes of this region are also the least known (Böhlke et al., 1978). Because of this, in the groups now being systematically studied, as for example families Callichthyidae, Cichlidae, Loricariidae, and Rivulidae, the number of described species is increasing rapidly.

Among the Rivulidae, the subfamily Cynolebiatinae has been the object of a series of taxonomic studies, exemplifying the above remarks. Fifty per cent of the known species were described in the last five years. This sudden advance is due also to changes in field work strategies. The Cynolebiatinae are annual fishes that only can be found in temporary aquatic environments during rainy seasons. During dry seasons, all fishes die and their eggs undergo diapause until the following wet season. Such processes also occur in South American fishes of the subfamily Rivulinae and in some representatives of the African family Aplocheilidae. This life cycle makes it difficult for collectors, who prefer to collect freshwater fishes during dry seasons because of the larger concentration of specimens at that time and the facility of travel along the access ways to the aquatic environments. Moreover, the different areas have distinct rainfall cycles. Thus, it is possible to determine the actual range of the group and the total number of species present only by collecting in the temporary swamps after analyzing the previous knowledge of regional rainfall cycles. The adoption of such activities quickly enlarged the known range of the Cynolebiatinae (Fig. 1).

Popular names for species of Cynolebiatinae are known only in the semi arid region of northeastern Brazil (Carvalho, 1957). These are applicable to the large species of the "*Cynolebias porosus* complex" that are used as food by the local population. Here the fishes are called *peixes-de-nuvem* (from the Portuguese meaning fish from clouds), because the natives attribute their abrupt appearance in areas where before there was no life nor water to the spontaneous generation of fishes in the clouds.

The 55 species of the eight genera of the subfamily Cynolebiatinae differ from each other in several aspects. Some species do not surpass 25 mm in standard length (ex. *Plesiolebias lacerdai*), while others reach more than 120 mm SL (ex. *Cynolebias elongatus*). The males frequently have brilliant colors, and sometimes even possess exotic fin shapes. These characteristics have awakened the interest of aquarists, who often organize associations, some of which publish specialized journals (e.g., *Deutsche Killifisch Gemeinschaft* and *Journal of the American Killifish Association*).

Unfortunately, the set of conditions

related to the peculiar life cycle of the Cynolebiatinae that captivates scientists and aquarists is also the factor that causes these fishes to become the greatest victims of economic development among Neotropical organisms. Many kinds of undertakings in expansion in South America menace the habitat of the Cynolebiatinae. Deforestation, river barriers, drainage systems, and embankments all destroy in an irreversible way the temporary environments, threatening the very existence of several of these species.

METHODS

In the systematic section diagnoses of genera include autapomorphies of the genera; diagnoses of species include characters that distinguish the taxon from all other congeneric species; descriptions of genera include characters of some importance for

phylogenetic analysis of the family Rivulidae (discussed in Costa, 1990a; 1991; and in the phylogenetic section of the present study); and descriptions of species include morphological characters such as coloration and fin shape and position, as well as those characters used in the diagnoses of the species.

Methods for taking measurements and counts follow Costa (1988a, 1990a), as illustrated in Figure 2. Measurements are presented as percentages of standard length (SL), except the eye diameter and the distance between the supraorbital series are presented as percentages of the head length (HL).

The osseous and cartilaginous skeletal elements were examined in cleared and counterstained specimens prepared following the method of Dingerkus & Uhler (1977). In anatomical illustrations areas with dots represent bone and areas with

Fig. 2. Measurements taken on rivulids. A, standard length; B, head length; C, head depth; D, body depth; E, depth of caudal peduncle; F, predorsal length; G, preanal length; H, prepelvic length; I, length of dorsal fin base; J, length of anal fin base; K, length of pectoral fin; L, length of caudal fin; M, eye diameter.

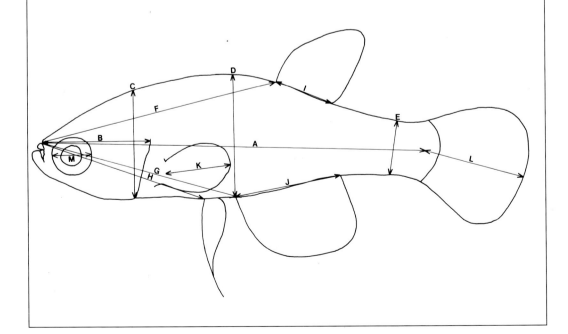

circles represent cartilage. Names for skeletal structures follow Costa (1990a).

Phylogenetic analysis follows the methods of phylogenetic systematics (Hennig, 1950; Wiley, 1981; Farris, 1983; Maddison et al. 1984).

Biogeographic analysis is according to the basic procedures of the "biogeographic parsimony analysis" (Brooks, 1981). Terminal taxa and redundant groups are not codified. Areas of endemism are delimited according to the distribution of monophyletic groups. Thus, different sections of the same fluvial system may be included in different areas of endemism, and sections of different basins may be included in the same area.

HISTORY OF CYNOLEBIATINAE SYSTEMATICS

Steindachner (1876), in describing *Cynolebias porosus*, based on a specimen collected in Pernambuco, northeastern Brazil, was the author of the earliest record of a member of the Cynolebiatinae.

In the succeeding 35 years little was added to the systematics of the Cynolebiatinae. Even Garman (1895), who published an extensive revision of the fishes of the order Cyprinodontiformes in which several Neotropical species of the families Rivulidae (only Rivulinae), Poeciliidae, and Cyprinodontidae were described, had no new data about the Cynolebiatinae. In this period only two species were described from northeastern Argentina (Steindachner, 1881)

A new impetus to the taxonomy of the Cynolebiatinae was given by C. Tate Regan, who published a revision of *Cynolebias*, including two new species from northeastern Argentina and southern Brazil (Regan, 1912a),

followed by the description of the genus *Cynopoecilus* from southern Brazil (Regan, 1912b).

During the following two decades, E. Ahl published some studies (Ahl, 1922; 1924; 1934) that included the description of two new species from southern Brazil as well as some other species that are now considered synonyms of already described species from northeastern Argentina. At about the same time, Ladiges (1934) described *Cynopoecilus marmoratus* (now in genus *Leptolebias*), the first Cynolebiatinae from southeastern Brazil.

In the 1940s to 1950s, G. S. Myers published a series of papers on cynolebiatine fishes, including descriptions of new species from southern and southeastern Brazil (Myers, 1942; 1947), description of a new subgenus of *Cynolebias* (*Leptolebias*, now recognized as a valid genus) from southeastern Brazil (Myers, 1952), and information about habitats and coloration (Myers, 1944; 1952). Based on the new records obtained at this time, mainly in the Upper Iguassu and northeastern Brazil, Myers (1952) suggested that annual fishes of the genus *Cynolebias* could occur in the central regions of South America, including the Amazon. This was confirmed a few years later when Carvalho (1959) described a new genus, *Simpsonichthys*, from central Brazil, evidently closely related to *Cynolebias*. *Simpsonichthys* is now considered a junior synonym of *Cynolebias*.

Hoedeman (1960), studying the cephalic squamation patterns of cyprinodontiform fishes, erected the tribe Cynolebiatini (subfamily Cynolebiatinae in the present paper).

Ringuelet et al. (1967) expanded the known range of *Cynolebias*, adding records from the Chaco in northern Argentina.

Weitzman & Wourms (1967) described a new species, *Austrofundulus dolichopterus*, from Venezuela. *Austrofundulus* Myers, 1932, is an endemic genus from northern South America belonging to the subfamily Rivulinae. Taphorn & Thomerson (1978) suggested that the species could be related to *Cynolebias* and erected a new genus, *Terranatos*, for it. This proposal has been corroborated in more recent studies (Parenti, 1981; Costa, 1990a).

In the 1960s to 1970s, R. Vaz-Ferreira conducted some studies on the Cynolebiatinae, publishing papers that included the description of three new species from eastern Uruguay (Vaz-Ferreira et al., 1964), the description of a new genus, *Campellolebias*, from southern Brazil (Vaz-Ferreira & Sierra, 1974), new records (Vaz-Ferreira & Sierra, 1971), and comparative researches on their morphology and behavior (Vaz-Ferreira & Sierra, 1972; 1973).

Parenti (1981) was the first to present apomorphic characters defining the monophyly of the rivulid genera. She considered all of the genera of the Cynolebiatinae as synonyms of *Cynolebias*.

Costa (1990a) published a phylogenetic analysis of the Rivulidae, where *Terranatos*, *Leptolebias*, *Cynopoecilus*, and *Campellolebias* were considered valid genera. In other papers, 16 new species from northeastern, central, southeastern, and southern Brazil, and a new genus, *Plesiolebias*, from central Brazil, were described (Costa, 1988a, 1990b,c; Costa & Brasil, 1990, 1991; Costa & Lacerda, 1988a; Costa, Lacerda & Brasil, 1989, 1990; Costa, Lacerda & Tanizaki, 1988a).

Finally, during the 1960s and subsequent years, other authors have described 20 new species of Cynolebiatinae (Amato, 1986;

Carvalho, 1971; Carvalho & Cruz, 1987; Castello & Lopez, 1974; Cruz, 1974; Cruz & Peixoto, 1991; Lazara, 1991; Miller & Hubbs, 1974; Taberner et al., 1974; Tulipano, 1973) from southeastern Mexico, northeastern, central, eastern, and southern Brazil, northern and northeastern Argentina, and eastern, central, and southern Uruguay.

PHYLOGENY

In spite of some taxonomic studies covering the fishes of the subfamily Cynolebiatinae, until 1981 nothing was explicitly discussed about phylogenetic relationships or generic monophyly. In fact, even the distinctions of the genera were based on dubious characters. This chaotic condition was discussed in detail by Weitzman & Wourms (1967).

Parenti (1981) united all of the genera of the Cynolebiatinae in *Cynolebias*, which was diagnosed by having the caudal fin not scaled and the preopercular canal closed. She considered the sister group of the genus to be *Austrofundulus*.

In a reevaluation of the phylogeny of the Rivulidae, Costa (1990a) elevated *Cynolebias* (sensu Parenti, 1981) to subfamilial rank, which included the genera *Terranatos*, *Cynolebias*, *Leptolebias*, *Cynopoecilus*, and *Campellolebias*. In this study the Cynolebiatinae was hypothesized to be the sister group of all other rivulid genera that were placed in the subfamily Rivulinae.

Subsequent studies (Costa, 1990c, 1991), included the description of a new genus, *Plesiolebias*, and added new data to the Cynolebiatinae phylogeny. In the present study, having studied some species not available before, the previous general proposal is supported. However, I propose some alterations to this system which is expanded by the inclusion of two new genera, *Millerichthys* and *Maratecoara*.

Maratecoara has all the synapomorphies used by Costa (1990a) to diagnose the subfamily Cynolebiatinae, i.e., horizontal median line on caudal fin 30% or less scaled, preopercular canal absent, alveolar arm of premaxilla expanded, and symplectic elongate, but *Millerichthys* possesses only the first two. In *Millerichthys* the symplectic is somewhat deep and the alveolar arm of the premaxilla is moderate, as in the Rivulinae and other aplocheiloid fishes (Figs. 3-4). Such evidence suggests that *Millerichthys* is the sister group of all other Cynolebiatinae. Furthermore, *Millerichthys*, as well as the Rivulinae and Aplocheilidae, has a well developed ventral process of the posttemporal, whereas in the other genera of the Cynolebiatinae it is reduced or absent (Fig. 5).

In *Millerichthys* there is a frontal squamation pattern composed of regularly distributed reduced scales (Fig. 6), the female has black spots on the caudal fin base, and the dermosphenotic is reduced. The squamation pattern and the pigmentation of the female are unique among cynolebiatine fishes. But, dermosphenotic reduction also occurs in the assemblage comprising *Cynolebias*, *Leptolebias*, *Campellolebias*, and *Cynopoecilus*, and it is more parsimonious to consider it as homoplasic. Therefore, the three character states above are hypothesized as autapomorphies for *Millerichthys*. The only known species, *M. robustus*, was originally described in the genus *Rivulus*, but it does not present any of the autapomorphies of this genus (neural prezygapophyses of caudal vertebrae elongated and cleithrum anteriorly expanded) nor the synapomorphy of the Rivulinae (frontal

squamation pattern arranged in circular pattern) as recognized by Costa (1990a).

The only species of *Maratecoara* was described as *Cynolebias lacortei* because the author followed Parenti's (1981) proposal, but this species does not have the *Cynolebias* autapomorphies as defined in the present study. The elongate dorsal and anal fins of the *M. lacortei* male make this fish somewhat similar to *Terranatos dolichopterus*. However, this similarity is only superficial since in *M. lacortei* only some rays are elongate and posteriorly directed, while in *T. dolichopterus* the whole fin is elongate and vertically oriented. In fact, *Maratecoara* seems to be more closely related to *Plesiolebias*, *Cynolebias*, *Leptolebias*, *Campellolebias*, and *Cynopoecilus*, than to *Terranatos*.

According to Costa (1990a), four synapomorphies support a hypothesis of monophyly for the assemblage including *Plesiolebias*, *Cynolebias*, *Leptolebias*, *Campellolebias*, and *Cynopoecilus*: sharp upper tip of the preopercle, reduced anteroventral process of the anguloarticular, first vertebra without neural prezygapophysis, and lacrimal with reduced torsion and enlarged upper part (Costa, 1990a). *Maratecoara* has the first three synapomorphies but not the fourth (Figs. 4, 7-9). Also, *Maratecoara* does not have the autapomorphies of *Plesiolebias* nor the synapomorphies of the group composed of *Cynolebias*, *Leptolebias*, *Campellolebias*, and *Cynopoecilus*, as defined in the present study. *Maratecoara* is thus considered to be the sister group of *Plesiolebias*, *Cynolebias*, *Leptolebias*, *Campellolebias*, and *Cynopoecilus*.

Three autapomorphies define *Maratecoara*: male with supraoccipital process vertically

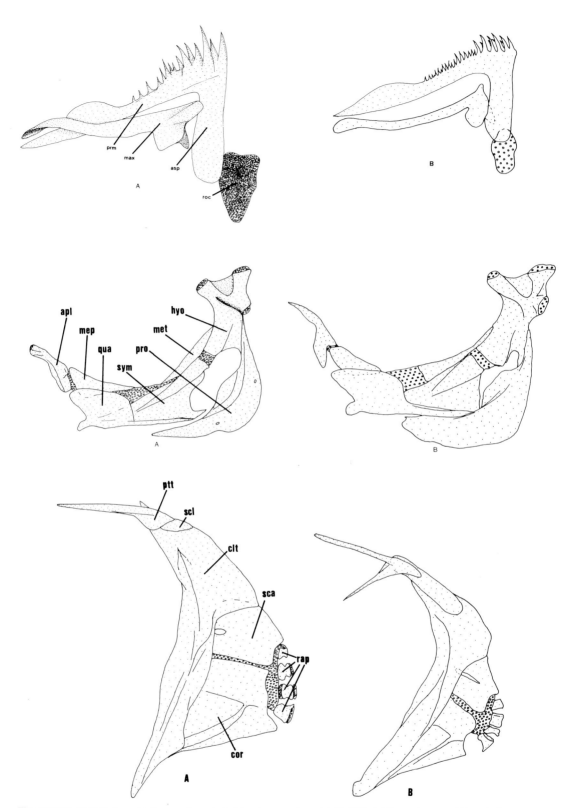

Fig. 3 (top). Dorsal view of left upper jaw of: A, *Maratecoara lacortei*; B, *Millerichthys robustus*. Abbreviations: asp: ascending process of premaxilla; max: maxilla; prm: premaxilla; roc: rostral cartilage. **Fig. 4 (middle).** Left jaw suspensorium (left lateral view) of: A, *Maratecoara lacortei*; B, *Millerichthys robustus*. Abbreviations: apl: autopalatine; hyo: hyomandibular; mep: mesopterygoid; met: metapterygoid; pro: preopercle; qua: quadrate; sym: sympletic. **Fig. 5 (bottom).** Left shoulder girdle (left lateral view) of: A, *Maratecoara lacortei*; B, *Millerichthys robustus*. Abbreviations: clt: cleithrum; cor: coracoid; ptt: post-temporal; rap: pectoral radials; sca: scapula; scl: supracleithrum.

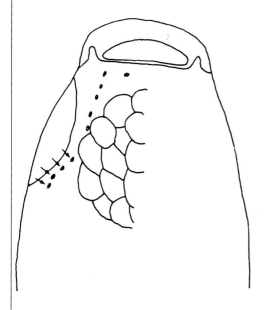

Fig. 6. Diagrammatic representation of the left part of the dorsal surface of the head of *Millerichthys robustus*. Arrows indicate neuromasts of posterior part of supraorbital series.

Furthermore, all genera of the subfamily Cynolebiatinae have a unique arrangement of the posterior supraoccipital neuromasts. In the Rivulinae and other cyprinodontiform fishes, the three principal neuromasts of that series are disposed in a triangle, whereas in species of Cynolebiatinae those neuromasts are aligned (Fig. 6).

The results of the studies covering the genera of Cynolebiatinae may be synthesized (Fig. 13) as follows:

All genera of Cynolebiatinae share three synapomorphies:
    (1) - Reduced caudal squamation;
    (2) - Posterior portion of supraorbital neuromasts aligned;
    (3) - Preopercular canal absent.

Terranatos, Maratecoara, Plesiolebias, Cynolebias, Leptolebias, Campellolebias, and *Cynopoecilus* share three synapomorphies:
    (4) - Symplectic elongated;
    (5) - Alveolar arm of premaxilla expanded;
    (6) - Ventral process of posttemporal reduced or absent.

Millerichthys has three autapomorphies:
    (7) - Dorsal surface of head with reduced scales;
    (8) - Female with dark spots on basal portion of caudal fin;
    (9) - Dermosphenotic reduced.

Maratecoara, Plesiolebias, Cynolebias, Leptolebias, Campellolebias, and *Cynopoecilus* share three synapomorphies:
    (10) - Upper tip of preopercle pointed;
    (11) - Anteroventral process of anguloarticular reduced;
    (12) - Neural prezygapophysis of first vertebra absent.

directed, branchiostegal membrane expanded (Figs. 10-11), and caudal fin strongly lanceolate and with elongated filamentous median rays. These do not occur in any other species of Aplocheiloidei.

There are two additional derived characters corroborating Costa's (1990a) proposed phylogeny for the Cynolebiatinae. The first one is the lack of vomerine teeth in the assemblage composed of *Cynolebias, Leptolebias, Campellolebias*, and *Cynopoecilus*. Vomerine teeth are present in all other rivulid genera. The second one is a plain shape to the inner facet of the first hypobranchial that occurs in the genera *Plesiolebias, Cynolebias, Leptolebias, Campellolebias*, and *Cynopoecilus*. Except for the rivuline genera *Moema* and *Trigonectes*, where the condition seems to be homoplasic, all other genera of Aplocheiloidei have a bifurcation in that facet (Fig. 12; compare with Fig. 36).

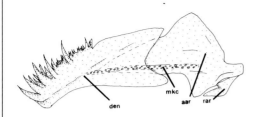

Fig. 7. Left lower jaw (left lateral view) of *Maratecoara lacortei*. Abbreviations: aar: angulo-articular; den: dentary; mkc: Meckel's cartilage; rar: retroarticular.

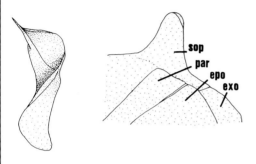

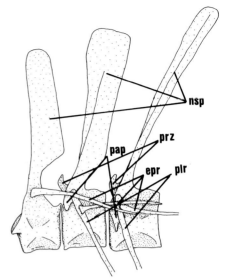

Fig. 8. First three vertebrae (left lateral view) of *Maratecoara lacortei*. Abbreviations: epr: epipleural ribs; nsp: neural spine; pap: parapophysis; plr: pleural rib; prz: neural prezygapophysis.

Fig. 12. Ventral gill arches (dorsal view) of *Maratecoara lacortei*. Abbreviations: bab: basibranchials; bah: basihyal; cbb: cartilaginous basibranchial 4; ceb: ceratobranchials; ceh: ceratohyal; dhh: dorsal hypohyal; hyb: hypobranchials; vhh: ventral hypohyal.

Fig. 9 (left). Left lacrimal of *Maratecoara lacortei*.
Fig. 10 (right). Posterior region of the skull in *Maratecoara lacortei*, left lateral view. Abbreviations: epo: epiotic; exo: exoccipital; par: parietal; sop: supraoccipital process.

Fig. 11. Left lateral view of head of *Maratecoara lacortei*. Abbreviations: brm: branchiostegal membrane; nds: neuromast on dermosphenotic; nps: neuromasts of the preopercular series; pef: pectoral fin.

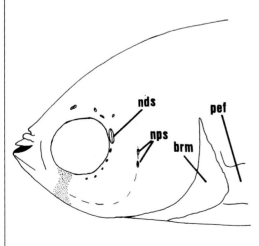

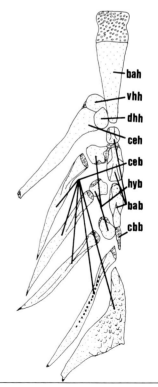

Terranatos has three autapomorphies:

(13) - Male with dorsal and anal fins vertically expanded;

(14) - Pectoral fin elongated;

(15) - Caudal fin of male with upper and lower posterior prolongations.

Plesiolebias, Cynolebias, Leptolebias, Campellolebias, and *Cynopoecilus* share two synapomorphies:

(16) - Lacrimal widened in upper portion and little twisted;

(17) - Inner facet of first hypobranchial plain.

Maratecoara has three autapomorphies:

(18) - Supraoccipital process of male vertically oriented;

(19) - Branchiostegal membrane widened in male;

(20) - Caudal fin of male strongly lanceolate and with elongated filamentous median rays.

Cynolebias, Leptolebias, Campellolebias, and *Cynopoecilus* share 11 synapomorphies:

(21) - Supracleithrum elongated;

(22) - Dermosphenotic reduced or absent;

(23) - Ceratobranchial 4 without teeth;

(24) - Ceratobranchial 4 without ventral process;

(25) - Neuromast on dermosphenotic reduced;

(26) - Supraorbital series of neuromasts united;

(27) - Mesopterygoid reduced;

(28) - Proximal anal radials widened;

(29) - Vomer without teeth;

(30) - Pectoral radials scale-like;

(31) - Caudal vertebrae without neural prezygapophyses.

Plesiolebias has four autapomorphies:

(32) - Basihyal elongated;

(33) - Horizontal process of quadrate elongated;

(34) - Pectoral fin reduced;

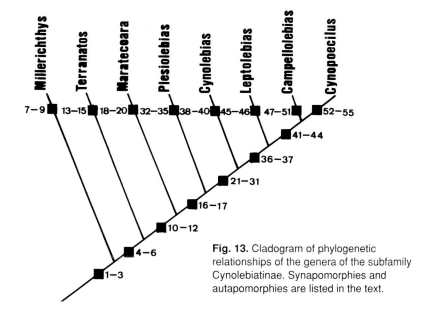

Fig. 13. Cladogram of phylogenetic relationships of the genera of the subfamily Cynolebiatinae. Synapomorphies and autapomorphies are listed in the text.

(35) - Interarcual cartilage absent.

Leptolebias, Campellolebias, and *Cynopoecilus* share two synapomorphies:
(36) - Mesial borders of anterocentral scalcs of dorsal surface of head not overlapping;
(37) - Egg with reticulate surface.

Cynolebias has three autapomorphies:
(38) - Male with more dorsal fin rays than female;
(39) - Female with black blotch on center of body sides;
(40) - Anal fin base of male enlarged.

Campellolebias and *Cynopoecilus* share four synapomorphies:
(41) - Caudal squamation well developed;
(42) - Pectoral fin reduced;
(43) - Pelvic fin base separated;
(44) - Proximal anal radials narrowed.

Leptolebias has two autapomorphies:
(45) - Posterodorsal surface of urohyal sinuous;
(46) - Female without dark markings on body sides.

Campellolebias has five autapomorphies:
(47) - Anterior portion of anal fin of male isolated;
(48) - Urogenital papilla of male elongated and connected to anal fin;
(49) - Ventral region of head of male with three longitudinal dark stripes;
(50) - Internal fertilization;
(51) - Chorion without prolongations.

Cynopoecilus has four autapomorphies:
(52) - Eight minute and close rays connected to first proximal radial of anal fin;
(53) - Urohyal slender;
(54) - Body sides with broad horizontal black stripe;
(55) - Male and female with similar color patterns.

SYSTEMATICS AND DISTRIBUTION

CYNOLEBIATINAE Hoedeman

Type genus: *Cynolebias* Steindachner.

   Diagnosis.- No preopercular canal; posterior portion of supraorbital series with aligned neuromasts; squamation on caudal fin base reduced (about 25% of caudal scaled along longitudinal axis).
   Eight genera are included.- *Millerichthys, Terranatos, Maratecoara, Plesiolebias, Cynolebias, Leptolebias, Cynopoecilus,* and *Campellolebias.*
   Distribution.- Middle America (Mexico) and South America (Venezuela, Brazil, Paraguay, Uruguay, and Argentina).

Key to the genera of Cynolebiatinae

1. - Neuromast on dermosphenotic not reduced; anterior and posterior portions of supraorbital series of neuromasts separated 2
   - Neuromast on dermosphenotic reduced; anterior and posterior portions of supraorbital series of neuromasts united 5

2. - Dorsal surface of head with scales not reduced; no distinctive spots on caudal fin base of female 3
   - Dorsal surface of head with reduced scales; female with distinctive spots on caudal fin base. .... *Millerichthys*

3. - Caudal fin of male never with upper and lower posterior prolongations; pectoral fin length 20-25% SL; origin of dorsal fin behind anal fin origin 4
   - Caudal fin of male with upper and lower posterior prolongations; pectoral fin length about 35% SL;

origin of dorsal fin in front of anal fin origin .... *Terranatos*

4. - Caudal fin of male lanceolate, with median rays filamentous; dorsal fin of male with long filamentous rays; branchiostegal membrane of male wide, reaching base of pectoral fin .... *Maratecoara*
   - Caudal fin of male rounded to somewhat truncate, never with filamentous rays; no filamentous rays in dorsal fin of male; branchiostegal membrane of male narrow, not reaching base of pectoral fin .... *Plesiolebias*

5. - Male and female with equal number of dorsal fin rays; antero-central scales not overlapping; no distinctive black blotch in center of body sides of female 6
   - Male with more dorsal fin rays than female; antero-central scales overlapping; female with distinctive black blotch in center of body sides .... *Cynolebias*

6. - Female with dark markings on body sides; origin of dorsal fin in front of anal fin origin; pelvic fins with separate bases 7
   - Female with homogeneous pale brown coloration on body sides, without dark markings; origin of dorsal fin behind anal fin origin; pelvic fins with united bases .... *Leptolebias*

7. - Eight minute and close rays connected to first proximal radial of anal fin; anterior portion of anal fin of male not isolated; urogenital papilla of male not elongated; body sides with wide horizontal black stripe; male and female with

similar color pattern; no longitudinal dark stripes on ventral region of head of male.

.... *Cynopoecilus*

- Anterior rays of anal fin not modified; anterior portion of anal fin of male isolated and connected to an elongate urogenital papilla; never a wide black stripe on body sides; male and female with distinctly different color pattern; male with three longitudinal dark stripes on ventral region of head.

.... *Campellolebias*

MILLERICHTHYS, new genus

Type species: *Rivulus robustus* Miller & Hubbs, 1974.

Diagnosis.- Dorsal surface of head with reduced scales; female with dark spots on basal portion of caudal fin; dermosphenotic reduced.

Description.- Anterior portion of anal fin of male not modified. Anal and dorsal fins moderate. Anal fin base of male about 23% SL. Caudal fin of male somewhat truncate, its length about 30% SL; about 25% of caudal scaled along longitudinal axis. Pectoral fin rounded, its length about 20% SL. Pelvic fins with united bases and seven rays. Male and female with same number of dorsal fin rays. Urogenital papilla moderate. Branchiostegal membrane moderate. Male reaching about 30 mm SL.

Dorsal surface of head with reduced scales not arranged in circular pattern. Mesial borders of anterocentral scales overlapping. Anterior and posterior portions of supraorbital series of neuromasts separate; anterior portion with six

neuromasts; posterior portion with five or six aligned neuromasts. Neuromast on dermosphenotic somewhat reduced. Preopercular canal absent.

Dentary moderate; dorsal and ventral surfaces not parallel. Ascending process of premaxilla narrow and without basal concavity. Vomer with two teeth. Anguloarticular with anteromedian process moderate and anteroventral process not reduced. Upper tip of quadrate without anterior expansion, posterior horizontal process moderate. Symplectic moderate. Mesopterygoid not reduced. Upper tip of preopercle somewhat wide and moderate in length.

Dermosphenotic reduced. Lacrimal moderate, narrow in upper portion and twisted. Supraoccipital process horizontally oriented. Urohyal moderate in depth, posterodorsal tip rounded. First epibranchial larger than second and third. Interarcual cartilage about 60% length of second epibranchial. No molariform teeth in branchial apparatus. Basihyal short and somewhat broad. Proximal edge of first

Fig. 14. Geographic distribution of *Millerichthys.*

hypobranchial bifid.

Thirteen precaudal and 19 caudal vertebrae. First vertebra with neural prezygapophysis. Neural prezygapophysis of caudal vertebrae moderate. Proximal radials of anal fin widened; second, third, and fourth not smaller than posterior proximal radials. Pectoral radials cubiform. Supracleithrum moderate. Lower tip of cleithrum without anterior expansion. Posttemporal with lower process well developed.

Male and female with distinct color pattern. Male with dark brown sides and three yellow transverse stripes on anal fin. Female with dark spots on basal portion of caudal fin.

Reproductive behavior and eggs unknown.

A unique species is included: *M. robustus* (Miller & Hubbs).

Distribution.- Papaloapan and Coatzacoalcos basins, coastal lowlands of southeastern Mexico (Fig. 14).

Etymology.- *Millerichthys* is named in honor of the American ichthyologist Robert Rush Miller. The gender is masculine.

Millerichthys robustus (**Miller & Hubbs**) **new combination** (Fig. 15)

Rivulus robustus Miller & Hubbs, 1974:865 (original description; basins of the Rios Papaloapan and Coatzacoalcos, southeastern Mexico).

Diagnosis.- As for the genus.

Description.- Dorsal and anal fins pointed in male, rounded in female. Posterior margin of pectoral fin reaches to pelvic fin base. Pelvic fin reaches to base of first anal fin ray in male and to urogenital papilla in female. Origin of dorsal fin opposite anal fin rays 6-7.

Coloration.- As described for the genus (known only from a short note in the original description).

Distribution.- As for the genus.

TERRANATOS Taphorn & Thomerson

Terranatos Taphorn & Thomerson, 1978:384 (type species *Austrofundulus dolichopterus* Weitzman & Wourms, 1967, by original designation).
Terranotus Parenti, 1981:367, 375, 379, 381-386, 490 (misspelling).
Terranotos Wildekamp, 1981:187, 199 (misspelling).

Diagnosis.- Male with dorsal and anal fins vertically expanded; pectoral fin elongated (about 35% SL); caudal fin with upper and lower posterior prolongations.

Description.- Anterior portion of anal fin of male not modified. Anal and dorsal fins of male vertically elongated. Length of anal fin base of male about

Fig. 15. *Millerichthys robustus,* paratype from Veracruz, male, 20 mm SL, UMMZ 194706.

15% SL. Caudal fin length of male about 35% SL (without expansions), with upper and lower posterior prolongations; about 25% of caudal scaled along longitudinal axis. Pectoral fin of male somewhat pointed, length about 35% SL. Pelvic fins with united bases and eight rays. Male and female with same number of dorsal fin rays. Urogenital papilla moderate. Branchiostegal membrane moderate. Male reaching about 30 mm SL.

Dorsal surface of head with scales neither reduced nor arranged in circular pattern. Mesial borders of anterocentral scales overlapping. Anterior and posterior portions of supraorbital series of neuromasts separate; anterior portion with five or six neuromasts; posterior portion with four aligned neuromasts. Neuromast on dermosphenotic not reduced. Preopercular canal absent.

Dentary moderate; dorsal and ventral surfaces not parallel. Ascending process of premaxilla narrow, without basal concavity. Vomer with a tooth. Anguloarticular with anteromedian process moderate and anteroventral process not reduced. Upper tip of quadrate without anterior expansion, posterior horizontal process moderate. Symplectic elongated. Mesopterygoid not reduced. Upper tip of preopercle somewhat wide, moderate in length.

Dermosphenotic not reduced. Lacrimal moderate, narrow in upper portion and twisted. Supraoccipital process horizontally oriented. Urohyal somewhat deep, posterodorsal tip rounded. First epibranchial larger than second and third. Interarcual cartilage about 60% of length of second epibranchial. No molariform teeth in branchial apparatus. Basihyal short and somewhat broad.

Proximal edge of first hypobranchial bifid.

Thirteen precaudal and 14 caudal vertebrae. First vertebra with neural prezygapophysis. Neural prezygapophysis of caudal vertebrae moderate. Proximal radials of anal fin wide; second, third, fourth, and posterior proximal radials approximately the same length. Pectoral radials cubiform. Supracleithrum moderate. Lower tip of cleithrum without anterior expansion. Posttemporal with reduced lower process.

Male and female with distinct color pattern. Males and females with spots on body sides.

Male during courtship with unpaired fins erected and twisted. Fertilization external. Egg diameter about 1.0 mm. Development annual.

A unique species is included: *T. dolichopterus* (Taphorn & Thomerson).

Distribution.- Middle Orinoco basin, central Venezuela (Fig. 16).

Fig. 16. Geographic distribution of *Terranatos* (asterisks) and *Maratecoara* (stars). Some symbols represent more than one collecting locality.

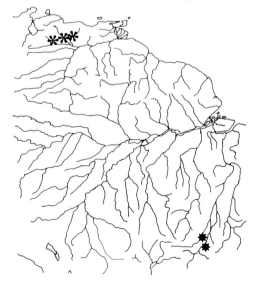

Fig. 17. *Terranatos dolichopterus,* aquarium fish. (K. Tanaka).

Terranatos dolichopterus
(Weitzman & Wourms)
(Fig. 17-18)

Austrofundulus dolichopterus Weitzman & Wourms, 1967:95 (original description, 40 km S El Pao, Cojedes, Venezuela). .

Terranatos dolichopterus Taphorn & Thomerson, 1978:381

Cynolebias dolichopterus Parenti, 1981:379.

Diagnosis.- As for the genus.

Description.- Dorsal and anal fins pointed. Caudal fin truncate, with upper and lower posterior prolongations. Posterior tip of pectoral fin reaches to base of tenth anal ray in male and to anus in female. Pelvic fin reaches to base of seventh anal ray in male and to base of third anal ray in female. Origin of anal fin opposite third dorsal ray.

Coloration.- Male: sides of body and unpaired fins pale blue with reddish brown spots. *Female*: sides of body pale brown with brown spots. Fins hyaline.

Distribution.- Middle Orinoco basin, States of Portuguesa, Guarico, and Apure, northwestern Venezuela.

MARATECOARA, new genus

Type species: *Cynolebias lacortei* Lazara, 1991.

Diagnosis.- Supraoccipital process of male vertically oriented; branchiostegal membrane widened in male; caudal fin of male strongly lanceolate and with elongated filamentous median rays.

Description.- Anterior portion of anal fin of male not modified. Anal and dorsal fins of male with elongated filamentous rays. Length of anal fin base of male about 25% SL. Caudal fin of male strongly lanceolate, with elongated filamentous median rays, length about 50% SL; about 20% of caudal scaled along longitudinal axis.

Fig. 18. *Terranatos dolichopterus,* aquarium fish. (E. Taylor)

Pectoral fin somewhat pointed, length about 25% SL. Pelvic fins with united bases and eight rays. Male and female with same number of dorsal fin rays. Urogenital papilla moderate. Branchiostegal membrane wide in males, reaching to base of pectoral fin rays. Male reaching about 30 mm SL.

Dorsal surface of head with scales neither reduced nor arranged in circular pattern. Mesial borders of anterocentral scales overlapping. Anterior and posterior portions of supraorbital series of neuromasts separate; anterior portion with five neuromasts; posterior portion with four aligned neuromasts. Neuromast on dermosphenotic not reduced. Preopercular canal absent.

Dentary moderate; dorsal and ventral surfaces not parallel. Ascending process of premaxilla narrow, without basal concavity. Vomer with one or two teeth. Anguloarticular with anteromedian process moderate and anteroventral process reduced. Upper tip of quadrate without anterior expansion, posterior horizontal process not elongated. Symplectic elongated. Mesopterygoid not reduced. Upper tip of preopercle sharp and moderate.

Dermosphenotic not reduced. Lacrimal moderate, not widened in upper portion and twisted. Supraoccipital process vertically oriented in male. Urohyal moderate in depth, with rounded posterodorsal tip. First, second, and third epibranchials of the same length. Interarcual cartilage about 60% length of second epibranchial. No molariform teeth in branchial apparatus. Basihyal short and somewhat narrow. Proximal edge of first hypobranchial bifid.

Twelve to 13 precaudal and 15 caudal vertebrae. First vertebra with neural prezygapophysis. Neural prezygapophysis of caudal vertebrae moderate. Proximal radials of anal fin widened; second, third, and fourth not smaller than posterior proximal radials. Pectoral radials cubiform. Supracleithrum moderate. Lower tip of cleithrum without anterior expansion. Posttemporal with reduced lower process.

Male and female with distinct color pattern. Male and female with dark spots on anterodorsal region of body sides.

Male during courtship with unpaired fins erected and twisted. Fertilization external. Egg with surface not reticulate and with thornlike prolongations. Egg diameter 1.0 mm. Development annual.

A unique species is included: *M. lacortei* (Lazara).

Distribution.- Upper Araguaia basin, central Brazil (Fig. 16).

Maratecoara lacortei (Lazara), new combination
(Fig. 19-20)

Cynolebias lacortei Lazara, 1991:141 (original description; temporary pool, Aruanã, Goiás, Brazil).

Diagnosis.- As for the genus.

Description.- Dorsal and anal fins pointed. Posterior margin of pectoral fin reaches to base of anal fin rays 3-5 in male, and to urogenital papilla in female. Pelvic fin reaches to base of anal fin rays 4-6 in male, and to base of anal fin rays 1-2 in female. Origin of dorsal fin opposite anal fin rays 3-5 in male, and anal fin rays 1-2 in female.

Coloration.- *Male*: head and body sides purplish blue, with orange spots that are more concentrated in anterodorsal region of body sides and dorsal and opercular regions of head. Dorsal fin purplish blue with red upper rays. Anal and caudal fins bluish. *Female*: head and body sides pale brown with dark dots in anterodorsal region. Fins hyaline.

Distribution.- Upper Araguaia and Rio das Mortes basins, Mato Grosso and Goiás, central Brazil.

Fig. 19 (above). *Maratecoara lacortei*, wild male from swamp near Rio das Mortes, about 25 mm SL, not preserved. Photo by G. Brasil.

Fig. 20 (below). *Maratecoara lacortei*, aquarium fish. (K. Tanaka)

PLESIOLEBIAS Costa

Plesiolebias Costa, 1990c:193 (type
  species *Cynolebias xavantei* Costa,
  Lacerda & Tanizaki, 1988a, by
  original designation).

Diagnosis. - Basihyal elongated and
narrow; quadrate with posterior
horizontal process elongated; pectoral
fin reduced, about 20% SL; interarcual
cartilage absent.

Description. - Anterior portion of
anal fin of male not modified. Anal and
dorsal fins moderate. Length of anal
fin base of male 19.5-28.5% SL.
Caudal fin of male rounded, length
about 35% SL; about 30% of caudal
scaled along longitudinal axis. Pectoral
fins rounded, length about 20% SL.
Pelvic fins with united bases and seven
rays. Male and female with same
number of dorsal fin rays. Urogenital
papilla moderate. Branchiostegal
membrane moderate. Male reaching
about 35 mm SL.

Dorsal surface of head with scales
neither reduced nor arranged in
circular pattern. Mesial borders of
anterocentral scales overlapping.
Anterior and posterior portions of
supraorbital series of
neuromasts separate; anterior
portion with five or six
neuromasts; posterior portion
with four aligned neuromasts.
Neuromast on dermosphenotic
not reduced. Preopercular
canal absent.

Dentary moderate; dorsal
and ventral surfaces not
parallel. Ascending process of
premaxilla narrow, without
basal concavity. Vomer with a
tooth. Anguloarticular with
anteromedian process
moderate, anteroventral
process reduced. Upper tip of
quadrate without anterior
expansion and posterior

horizontal process elongated.
Symplectic elongated. Mesopterygoid
not reduced. Upper tip of preopercle
sharp and moderate.

Dermosphenotic not reduced.
Lacrimal moderate, widened in upper
portion and little twisted.
Supraoccipital process horizontally
oriented. Urohyal moderate in depth,
posterodorsal tip rounded. First
epibranchial larger than second and
third. Without interarcual cartilage. No
molariform teeth in branchial
apparatus. Basihyal elongated and
narrow. Proximal edge of first
hypobranchial not bifid.

Twelve precaudal and 12-14 caudal
vertebrae. First vertebra without
neural prezygapophysis. Neural
prezygapophysis of caudal vertebrae
moderate. Proximal radials of anal fin
widened; second, third, and fourth not
smaller than posterior proximal
radials. Pectoral radials cubiform.
Supracleithrum moderate. Lower tip of
cleithrum without anterior expansion.

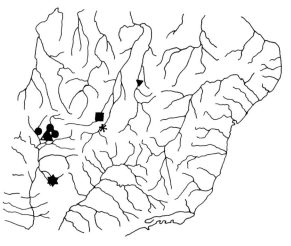

Fig. 21. Geographic distribution of *Plesiolebias* (some
symbols represent more than one collecting locality).
Black triangle: *P. xavantei*; square: *P. aruana*; circles:
P. glaucopterus; asterisk: *P. lacerdai*; open triangle:
P. damascenoi; star: *P. bellus*.

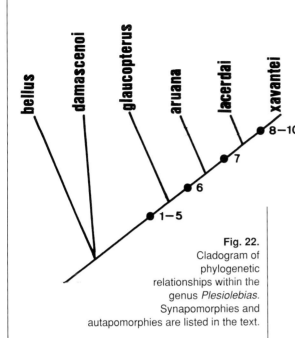

Fig. 22. Cladogram of phylogenetic relationships within the genus *Plesiolebias*. Synapomorphies and autapomorphies are listed in the text.

Posttemporal without lower process.

Male and female with distinct color pattern. Male and female with dark oblique bars on body sides or without markings.

Male during courtship with open unpaired fins. Fertilization external. Egg without reticulations on surface and with thornlike prolongations. Egg diameter about 0.9 mm. Development annual.

Six species are included: *P. bellus*, *P. damascenoi*, *P. glaucopterus*, *P. aruana*, *P. lacerdai*, and *P. xavantei*.

Distribution. - Paraguay and Araguaia-Tocantins basins (Fig. 21).

Generic Intrarelationships. - Phylogenetic relationships of *Plesiolebias* species were recently analyzed by Costa (1991). The following scheme follows that paper, but includes two additional species, *P. aruana* and *P. bellus*. Numbers in parenthesis refer to apomorphic states of the cladogram of Figure 22.

Plesiolebias glaucopterus, P. aruana, P. lacerdai, and *P. xavantei* share five synapomorphies:

(1) - 24-25 vertebrae. All other Cynolebiatinae species have 26-37 vertebrae.

(2) - Female larger than male. In all other Rivulidae species the male is larger than female.

(3) - Male with tips of dorsal and anal fins rounded. In other species of Cynolebiatinae anal and dorsal fins of male are pointed, except in *Cynolebias bellottii* and closely related species. This apomorphic condition is considered independently acquired in the two groups.

(4) - Male with a red horizontal stripe posterior to eye, a color pattern unique among the Cynolebiatinae.

(5) - Male with oblique reddish bars alternating with brilliant spots on body sides. This color pattern is unique among the Cynolebiatinae.

Plesiolebias aruana, P. lacerdai, and *P. xavantei* share one synapomorphy:

(6) - Head width of male 16.1-17.9% SL. In other species of *Plesiolebias* and related genera, head width of male is 18.2% SL or more.

Plesiolebias lacerdai and *P. xavantei* share one synapomorphy:

(7) - Male with black horizontal stripes in anterior region of body sides. This color pattern is unique among the Cynolebiatinae.

Plesiolebias xavantei has three evident autapomorphies:

(8) - Supraoccipital process reaching neural spine of first vertebra. In other species of Cynolebiatinae such a process never reaches neural spine of first vertebra.

(9) - First two proximal radials of anal fin fused. This apomorphic condition is unique among *Plesiolebias* and closely related genera.

(10) - Tip of pelvic fin of male reaching base of 13th anal fin ray. In other Cynolebiatinae the male's pelvic fin tip reaches only to anal fin rays 1-5.

Key to the Species of *Plesiolebias*

1. - Dorsal and anal fins pointed in male; sixteen horizontal scale rows around caudal peduncle; male without a red horizontal stripe posterior to eye 2
   - Dorsal and anal fins rounded in male; twelve horizontal scale rows around caudal peduncle; male with a red horizontal stripe posterior to eye................. 3
2. - Male with dark oblique bars on sides; dorsal fin of male greenish yellow with black spots; anal fin of male greenish yellow, with alternating dark brown and white spots on basal region .... *P. bellus*
   - Male without bars on sides; dorsal fin of male red with a black spot edged with bright blue; anal fin of male pale blue, without spots .... *P. damascenoi*
3. - Head width of male 16.1-17.9% SL; anal fin base of male with alternate black and white transverse stripes 4
   - Head width of male 18.2-19.0% SL; anal fin base of male with alternate black and white spots. .... *P. glaucopterus*
4. - Origin of dorsal fin opposite anal fin rays 1-5; tip of pelvic fin of male reaches to base of anal fin rays 5-14; male with black oblique bars in anterior region of sides; male without bars in caudal fin 5
   - Origin of dorsal fin opposite anal fin rays 7-8; tip of pelvic fin of male reaches to base of anal fin rays 2-3; male without black oblique bars in anterior region of sides; male with dark gray bars in caudal fin .... *P. aruana*
5. - Male not reaching 25 mm SL; tip of pelvic fin of male reaches base of fifth anal fin ray .... *P. lacerdai*
   - Male reaches 35 mm SL; tip of pelvic fin of male reaches base of anal fin rays 9-13 .... *P. xavantei*

Fig. 23. *Plesiolebias bellus*, holotype at the moment of collection, male, 16.5 mm SL, MZUSP 42310. Photo by the author.

Plesiolebias bellus, new species
(Fig. 23)

Holotype. - MZUSP 42310, male, 16.5 mm SL; Brazil: Mato Grosso do Sul: about 5 km south of the city of Miranda, temporary flood plains of Rio Miranda, Rio Paraguay basin; W. J. E. M. Costa, C. P. Bove, M. Melgaço & F. A. Bockmann, 18 III 1991.

Paratypes. - MZUSP 42311, female, 13.0 mm SL; collected with the holotype. - UFRJ 385, male, 15.5 mm SL; UFRJ 386, female, 15.0 mm SL (cleared and counterstained); same locality and collectors, 21 III 1991.

Diagnosis. - Dorsal and anal fins pointed in male; sixteen horizontal scale rows around caudal peduncle; body sides of male with five dark oblique bars, dorsal fin greenish yellow with two rows of black spots, and anal fin greenish yellow with alternate black and white spots in basal region.

Description. - Dorsal and anal fins pointed in male, rounded in female. Caudal fin rounded. Posterior margin of pectoral fin reaches to the anus in male and to the pelvic fin base in female. Pelvic reaches to base of anal fin rays 2-3 in male and to urogenital papilla in female. Origin of dorsal fin opposite anal fin rays 7-8. Meristic and morphometric data are given in Table 1.

Coloration. - *Male*: sides of body golden in anterior region, pale purplish brown in median and posterior regions; five oblique faint brown bars. Sides of head golden. Iris orange; eye crossed by a black bar. Dorsal fin pale greenish yellow, with two transverse rows of black spots. Anal fin greenish yellow with alternate dark brown and white spots on basal region and black rays on distal region. Pelvic fins greenish yellow. Caudal fin slightly pink. Pectoral fins hyaline. *Female*: sides of body and head pale brown. Fins hyaline.

Distribution. - Middle Rio Paraguay flood plains, Mato Grosso do Sul, central Brazil.

Etymology. - From the Latin *bellus* (beautiful), an allusion to the beauty of the male of the species. An adjective.

Plesiolebias damascenoi Costa
(Figs. 24-25)

Plesiolebias damascenoi Costa, 1991 : 375 (original description; temporary pool, Poconé-Porto Cercado road, Mato Grosso, Brazil).

Diagnosis. - Dorsal and anal fins pointed in male; sixteen horizontal scale rows around caudal peduncle; male without bars on body sides, dorsal fin red with a blue-edged black spot, and anal fin pale blue.

Description. - Dorsal and anal fins pointed in male, rounded in female. Caudal fin rounded. Posterior margin of pectoral fin reaches to pelvic fin base. Pelvic reaches to base of anal fin rays 2-4 in male and to urogenital papilla in female. Origin of dorsal fin opposite anal fin rays 6-7. Sixteen horizontal scale rows around caudal

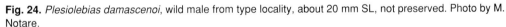

Fig. 24. *Plesiolebias damascenoi,* wild male from type locality, about 20 mm SL, not preserved. Photo by M. Notare.

Fig. 25. *Plesiolebias damascenoi*, wild female from type locality, about 20 mm SL, not preserved. Photo by M. Notare.

peduncle.

Coloration. - *Male*: sides of body light purplish brown. Dorsal fin red with posteriorly positioned black spot edged with bright blue. Anal fin bluish. Caudal fin hyaline. *Female*: sides of body pale brown with dark dots in dorsal region. Unpaired fins hyaline.

Distribution. - Upper Rio Paraguay flood plains, Mato Grosso, central Brazil.

Plesiolebias glaucopterus
(Costa & Lacerda)
(Figs. 26-27)

Cynolebias glaucopterus Costa & Lacerda, 1988a:16 (original description, temporary pool, Cáceres, Mato Grosso, Brazil).

Cynolebias pantanalensis Seegers, 1988:31 (original description, Transpantaneira road, Mato Grosso, Brazil).

Plesiolebias glaucopterus; Costa, 1990c:194.

Diagnosis. - Dorsal and anal fins rounded in male; twelve horizontal scale rows around caudal peduncle; head width of male 18.2-19.5% SL; male with oblique stripes on body sides, a red horizontal stripe posterior to eye, and alternate black and white spots on basal region of anal fin.

Description. - Dorsal and anal fins rounded. Caudal fin rounded. Posterior margin of pectoral fin reaches to urogenital papilla in male and to pelvic fin base in female. Pelvic fin reaches to base of anal fin rays 1-3 in male and to urogenital papilla in female. Origin of dorsal fin opposite seventh anal fin ray. Twelve horizontal scale rows around caudal peduncle. Head width of male 18.2-19.5% SL.

Coloration. - *Male*: sides of body greenish blue with red oblique bars and red horizontal stripe posterior to eye. Dorsal fin hyaline with dark gray and white spots. Anal fin greenish blue with black and white spots on basal region. Caudal fin hyaline with

Fig. 26 (above). *Plesiolebias glaucopterus*, wild male from type locality, about 20 mm SL, not preserved. Photo by G. Brasil.
Fig. 27 (below). *Plesiolebias glaucopterus*, wild female from type locality, about 25 mm SL, not preserved. Photo by G. Brasil.

brilliant green dots. *Female*: sides of body pale brown with oblique rows of dark dots. Unpaired fins hyaline.

Distribution. - Upper Rio Paraguay flood plains, Mato Grosso, central Brazil.

Plesiolebias aruana (Lazara)
new combination
(Fig. 28)

Cynolebias aruana Lazara, 1991:147 (original description, temporary pool, Aruanã, Goiás, Brazil).

Diagnosis - Dorsal and anal fins rounded in male; twelve horizontal scale rows around caudal peduncle; head width of male 16.2-17.2% SL; male with oblique stripes on body sides, a red horizontal stripe posterior to eye, alternate black and white spots on basal region of anal fin, and dark gray bars in caudal fin; origin of dorsal fin opposite anal fin rays 7-8; tip of pelvic fin of male reaches to base of anal fin rays 2-3.

Description - Dorsal and anal fins rounded. Caudal fin rounded. Posterior margin of pectoral fin reaches to base of first anal fin ray in male and to pelvic fin base in female. Pelvic fin reaches to base of anal fin

rays 1-3 in male and to urogenital papilla in female. Origin of dorsal fin opposite anal fin rays 7-8. Twelve horizontal scale rows around caudal peduncle. Head width of male 16.2-17.2% SL.

Coloration - Male: sides of body green with pink oblique bars and a red horizontal stripe posterior to eye. Dorsal fin hyaline with dark gray and green stripes in basal region. Anal fin gray with alternate black and white stripes in basal region. Caudal fin hyaline with dark gray bars. *Female*: sides of body pale brown with oblique rows of dark spots. Unpaired fins hyaline.

Distribution - Upper Rio Araguaia flood plains, Goiás, central Brazil.

Plesiolebias lacerdai Costa
(Fig. 29)

Plesiolebias lacerdai Costa, 1990c:196 (original description; vicinity of Rio das Mortes, Cocalinhos, Brazil).

Diagnosis. - Dorsal and anal fins rounded in male; twelve horizontal scale rows around caudal peduncle; head width of male 16.1-17.9% SL; male with black oblique stripes in anterior region of body sides, a red

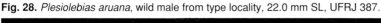

Fig. 28. *Plesiolebias aruana*, wild male from type locality, 22.0 mm SL, UFRJ 387.

Fig. 29. *Plesiolebias lacerdai*, paratypes, male above, 13.2 mm SL, female below, 16.5 mm Sl, MCP 12799.

horizontal stripe posterior to eye, alternate black and white spots on basal region of anal fin, and no bars in caudal fin; origin of dorsal fin opposite anal fin rays 1-3; tip of pelvic fin of male reaches to base of fifth anal fin ray; male reaching about 20 mm SL.

Description. - Dorsal and anal fins rounded. Caudal fin rounded. Posterior margin of pectoral fin reaches to base of third anal fin ray in male and to urogenital papilla in female. Pelvic fin reaches to base of fifth anal fin ray in male and to urogenital papilla in female. Origin of dorsal fin opposite anal fin rays 1-3. Twelve horizontal scale rows around caudal peduncle. Head width of male 16.1-17.9% SL. Male reaching about 20 mm SL.

Coloration. - *Male*: sides of body pale greenish brown with black oblique bars in anterior region and reddish bars in posterior region, both sets of bars interspersed by oblique rows of brilliant green dots. A faint red horizontal stripe posterior to eye.

Dorsal fin reddish brown with transverse white stripes. Anal fin dark gray with transverse white stripes in basal region. Caudal fin hyaline with greenish dots in basal region. *Female*: sides of body pale brown with dark oblique bars. Unpaired fins hyaline.

Distribution. - Rio das Mortes flood plains, Mato Grosso, central Brazil.

Plesiolebias xavantei
(Costa, Lacerda & Tanizaki)
(Fig. 30)

Cynolebias xavantei Costa, Lacerda & Tanizaki, 1988 :123 (original description, temporary pool near Porto Nacional, Goiás [now Tocantins], Brazil).
Plesiolebias xavantei; Costa, 1990 :194.

Diagnosis. - Dorsal and anal fins rounded in male; twelve horizontal scale rows around caudal peduncle; head width of male 16.5-17.9% SL; male with black oblique stripes in anterior region of body sides, a red horizontal stripe posterior to eye, alternate black and white spots on basal region of anal fin, and no bars in caudal fin; origin of dorsal fin opposite anal fin rays 3-5; tip of pelvic fin of male reaches to base of anal fin rays 9-13; male reaching about 35 mm SL.

Description. - Dorsal and anal fins rounded. Caudal fin rounded. Posterior margin of pectoral fin reaches to base of first anal fin ray in male and to urogenital papilla in female. Pelvic fin reaches to base of anal fin rays 9-13 in male and to anal fin rays 1-3 in female. Origin of dorsal fin opposite anal fin rays 3-5. Twelve horizontal scale rows around caudal peduncle. Head width of male 16.5-17.9% SL. Male reaching about 35 mm SL.

Coloration. - *Male*: sides of body purplish gray with black oblique bars in anterior region and reddish bars in posterior region, both bars interspersed by oblique rows of bluish green dots. A red horizontal stripe posterior to eye. Dorsal fin red with transverse white stripes. Anal fin dark gray with transverse white stripes in basal region. Caudal fin red with greenish dots in basal region. *Female*: sides of body pale brown with dark oblique bars. Unpaired fins hyaline.

Distribution. - Middle Rio Tocantins flood plains, Tocantins, central Brazil.

Fig. 30. *Plesiolebias xavantei*, wild male from type locality, 25.0 mm SL, not preserved. The dorsal fin is damaged and in part regenerated. Photo by J. Alves

CYNOLEBIAS Steindachner

Cynolebias Steindachner, 1876:172
(type species Cynolebias porosus
Steindachner, 1876, by original
designation).
Simpsonichthys Carvalho, l959:2 (type
species Simpsonichthys boitonei
Carvalho, 1959, by original
designation).

Diagnosis.- Male with more dorsal
fin rays than female; female with black
blotch on center of body sides; length
of anal fin base of male 30.0-55.0%
SL.

Description.- Anterior portion of anal
fin of male not modified. Anal and
dorsal fins moderate in length. Length
of anal fin base of male 30.0-55.0%
SL. Caudal fin of male rounded to
truncate, length about 35% SL; about
25% of caudal scaled along
longitudinal axis. Pectoral fin pointed
or rounded; length about 30% SL.
Pelvic fins with united bases and five
or six rays. Male with more dorsal fin
rays than female. Urogenital papilla
moderate. Branchiostegal membrane
moderate. Male reaching about 120
mm SL.

Dorsal surface of head with scales
neither reduced nor arranged in
circular pattern. Mesial borders of
anterocentral scales overlapping.
Anterior and posterior portions of
supraorbital series of neuromasts
united; anterior portion with six to 21
neuromasts; posterior portion with six
to 18 aligned neuromasts. Neuromast
on dermosphenotic reduced.
Preopercular canal absent.

Dentary moderate; dorsal and
ventral surfaces not parallel.
Ascending process of premaxilla
narrow and without concavity in base.
Vomer without teeth. Anguloarticular
with anteromedian process moderate
and anteroventral process reduced.
Upper tip of quadrate without anterior

expansion and posterior horizontal
process moderate. Symplectic
elongated. Mesopterygoid reduced.
Upper tip of preopercle sharp and
moderate in length.

Dermosphenotic absent. Lacrimal
moderate, widened in upper portion
and little twisted. Supraoccipital
process horizontally oriented. Urohyal
moderate in depth and with rounded
postero-dorsal tip. First epibranchial
larger than second and third.
Interarcual cartilage about 60% of
length of second epibranchial. No
molariform teeth in branchial
apparatus. Basihyal short and broad.
Proximal edge of first hypobranchial
not bifid.

Eleven to 15 precaudal and 16 to 22
caudal vertebrae. First precaudal and
caudal vertebrae without neural
prezygapophysis. Proximal radials of
anal fin wide; second, third, and
fourth smaller than posterior proximal
radials. Pectoral radials scale-like.
Supracleithrum elongated. Lower tip of
cleithrum without anterior expansion.
Posttemporal without lower process.

Male and female with distinct color
pattern. Male with dark bars or
longitudinal rows of dark spots or
transverse rows of bright dots on body
sides. Female with dark spots on body
sides and distinctive black blotch on
center of sides.

Male during courtship with open
unpaired fins. Fertilization external.
Egg without reticulation on surface
and with short thornlike
prolongations. Egg diameter 0.8-2.0
mm. Development annual.

Thirty-four species are included: C.
whitei, C. myersi, C. bokermanni, C.
constanciae, C. notatus, C. flammeus,
C. magnificus, C. chacoensis, C.
flavicaudatus, C. antenori, C. zonatus,
C. boitonei, C. costai, C. carvalhoi, C.
luteoflammulatus, C. alexandri, C.
affinis, C. nigripinnis, C. gymnoventris,
C. nonoiuliensis, C. cinereus, C.

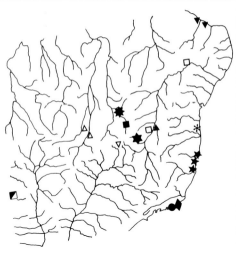

Fig. 31. Geographic distribution of some species of *Cynolebias* (some symbols represent more than one collecting locality). Black inverted triangle: *C. antenori*; open square: *C. flavicaudatus*; black triangle: *C. magnificus*; six tip star: *C. zonatus*; eight tip star: *C. flammeus*; black square: *C. notatus*; open triangle: *C. costai*; open inverted triangle: *C. boitonei*; asterisk: *C. bokermanni*; five tip star: *C. myersi*; circle: *C. whitei*; lozenge: *C. constanciae*; half black square: *C. chacoensis*.

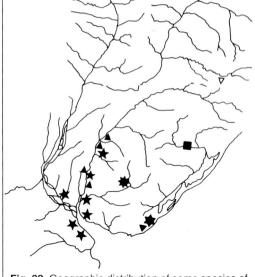

Fig. 32. Geographic distribution of some species of *Cynolebias* (some symbols represent more than one collecting locality). Open inverted triangle: *C. carvalhoi*; square: *C. cyaneus* (syn. of *affinis*); black triangle: *C. alexandri*; five tip star: *C. nigripinnis*; eight tip star: *C. affinis*; six tip star: *C. gymnoventris*; black inverted triangle: *C. luteoflammulatus*.

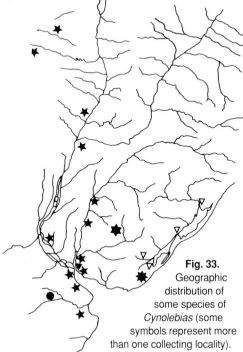

Fig. 33. Geographic distribution of some species of *Cynolebias* (some symbols represent more than one collecting locality). Five tip star: *C. bellottii*; open inverted triangle: *C. adloffi*; six tip star: *C. melanoorus*; black inverted triangle: *C. cinereus*; eight tip star: *C. viarius*; circle: *C. nonoiuliensis*.

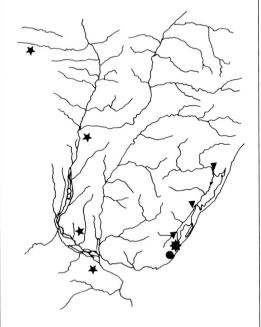

Fig. 34. Geographic distribution of some species of *Cynolebias* (some symbols represent more than one collecting locality). Five tip star: *C. elongatus*; triangle: *C. wolterstorffi*; eight tip star: *C. prognathus*; circle: *C. cheradophilus*.

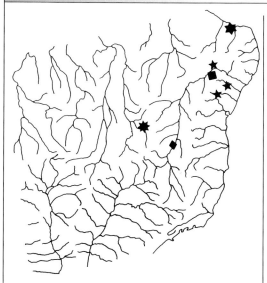

Fig. 35. Geographic distribution of some species of *Cynolebias* (some symbols represent more than one collecting locality). Six tip star: *C. microphthalmus*; five tip star: *C. porosus*; square: *C. albipunctatus*; eight tip star: *C. griseus*; lozenge: *C. perforatus*.

bellottii, *C. viarius*, *C. melanoorus*, *C. adloffi*, *C. cheradophilus*, *C. prognathus*, *C. wolterstorffi*, *C. elongatus*, *C. griseus*, *C. microphthalmus*, *C. perforatus*, *C. albipunctatus* and *C. porosus*.

Distribution.- São Francisco, Araguaia-Tocantins, Paraguay-Paraná basins, and isolated basins of northeastern, eastern, southeastern, and southern Brazil, and eastern Uruguay (Figs. 31-35).

Species Intrarelationships.- Numbers in parenthesis refer to apomorphic states of the cladogram of Figure 36.

Some monophyletic assemblages of closely related species of *Cynolebias* may be defined by apomorphic features. A group composed of *C. cheradophilus*, *C. prognathus*, *C. wolterstorffi*, and *C. elongatus*, here called the "*C. elongatus* complex," shares one synapomorphy:

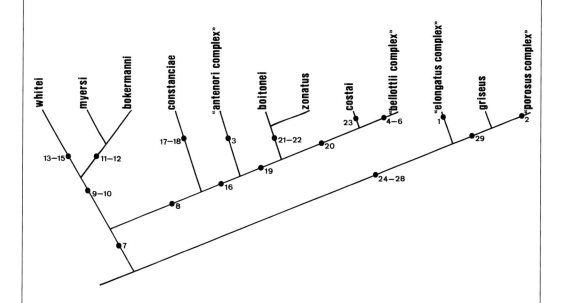

Fig. 36. Cladogram of phylogenetic relationships within the genus *Cynolebias*. Synapomorphies and autapomorphies are listed in the text.

(1) - Anal and dorsal fins gently pointed or rounded in male. In other closely related species these fins are strongly pointed in male, except in some species of the "*C. bellottii* complex." By parsimony, the state is considered homoplasic.

A group composed of *C. microphthalmus*, *C. perforatus*, *C. albipunctatus*, and *C. porosus*, here called the "*C. porosus* complex," shares one synapomorphy:

(2) - Anal fin of male with filamentous rays. In other species, the male has no filamentous rays in anal fin, except *C. constanciae*, *C. flavicaudatus*, *C. antenori*, and *C. chacoensis*, in which the state is considered to have been acquired independently.

A group composed of *C. chacoensis*, *C. flavicaudatus*, *C. antenori*, *C. magnificus*, *C. flammeus*, and *C. notatus*, here called the "*C. antenori* complex," shares one synapomorphy:

(3) - Predorsal length smaller than 48% SL. Predorsal length 52% SL or more in other species, except in *C. nigripinnis*, *C. affinis*, *C. cyaneus*, *C. alexandri*, *C. luteoflammulatus*, and *C. gymnoventris*, where it is considered an independent acquisition.

Fig. 37. Urohyal of *Cynolebias alexandri*, left lateral view.

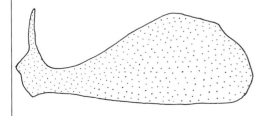

Fig. 38. Ventral gill arches of *Cynolebias adloffi*, dorsal view. Arrow indicates basihyal.

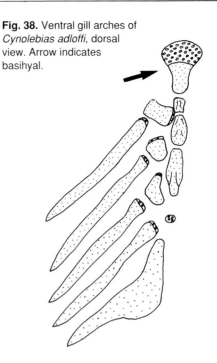

A group composed of *C. carvalhoi*, *C. luteoflammulatus*, *C. alexandri*, *C. cyaneus* (syn. of *affinis*), *C. affinis*, *C. nigripinnis*, *C. gymnoventris*, *C. nonoiuliensis*, *C. cinereus*, *C. bellottii*, *C. viarius*, *C. melanoorus*, and *C. adloffi*, here called the "*C. bellottii* complex," shares three synapomorphies:

(4) - Urohyal deep. In this group the urohyal is deeper than any other rivulid species (Fig. 37).

(5) - Bony part of basihyal reduced. In no other species of Rivulidae is this bony part so reduced (Fig. 38).

(6) - Upper pectoral radial very reduced or absent. Among aplocheiloid fishes, only representatives of the assemblage comprising the "*C. porosus* complex," the "*C. elongatus* complex," and *C. griseus* present this state. It is considered homoplasic for the two groups (Fig. 39).

Relationships of these complexes and other *Cynolebias* species are discussed below.

Cynolebias bokermanni, C. myersi, C. whitei, C. constanciae, species of the "*C. antenori* complex," *C. boitonei, C. zonatus, C. costai*, and species of the "*C. bellottii* complex" share one synapomorphy:

(7) - Preanal length smaller than 52% SL in male. In all other species of *Cynolebias* and closely related genera, preanal length is greater than 55% SL in male.

Cynolebias constanciae, species of the "*C. antenori* complex," *C. boitonei, C. zonatus, C. costai*, and species of the "*C. bellottii* complex" share one synapomorphy:

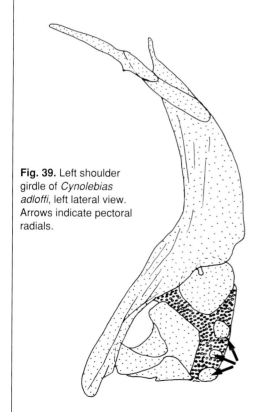

Fig. 39. Left shoulder girdle of *Cynolebias adloffi*, left lateral view. Arrows indicate pectoral radials.

(8) - Upper portion of cleithrum elongated. No other rivulid species has the cleithrum so elongated (Fig. 39).

Cynolebias bokermanni, C. myersi, and *C. whitei* share two synapomorphies:

(9) - Reduced head length (23-26% SL). In other species of *Cynolebias* and closely related genera, head length is about 30% SL.
(10) - Anal fin reddish in female. In other species of *Cynolebias* and closely related genera, anal fin of female is hyaline to yellowish.

Cynolebias bokermanni and *C. myersi* share two synapomorphies:

(11) - Caudal fin somewhat lanceolate in male. In other *Cynolebias* species the male's caudal fin is rounded or truncate.
(12) - Pectoral fin pointed in male. In other *Cynolebias* species pectoral fin of male is rounded.

Cynolebias whitei has three evident autapomorphies:

(13) - Pectoral fin of male with large papillae in inner surface;
(14) - Pectoral fin bluish with orange margin in male;
(15) - Anal fin with orange stripe with golden striae on distal edge. No other species of Cynolebiatinae has these states.

Species of the "*C. antenori* complex," *C. boitonei, C. zonatus, C. costai*, and species of the "*C. bellottii* complex" share one synapomorphy:

(16) - Length of dorsal fin base of male greater than 35% SL. In all other species of *Cynolebias* and closely related genera, dorsal fin base of male smaller than 32% SL, except in species of the "*C. bellottii* complex." By parsimony the states are considered homoplasic for the

two groups.

Cynolebias constanciae has two evident autapomorphies:

> (17) - Body sides of male with five rows of large black spots. This color pattern is unique among the Rivulidae.
>
> (18) - Eye diameter about 40% HL in male. In other *Cynolebias* species eye diameter of male 35% HL or less.

Cynolebias boitonei, C. zonatus, C. costai, and species of the "*C. bellottii* complex" share one synapomorphy:

> (19) - Five rays in pelvic fin. Other species of Cynolebiatinae have six to eight pelvic fin rays, except in *Leptolebias leitaoi,* which also has five rays. The reduced number of pelvic fin rays is considered independently acquired in the two groups.

Cynolebias costai and species of the "*C. bellottii* complex" share one synapomorphy:

> (20) - Length of greatest dorsal fin ray of male half or less length of anal fin base. In other Cynolebiatinae greatest dorsal fin ray of male greater than or almost equal to length of anal fin base.

Cynolebias boitonei and *C. zonatus* share two synapomorphies:

> (21) - Male with five red bars on side of head;
>
> (22) - Pelvic fin reduced (not reaching anal fin origin in male) or absent. No other Cynolebiatinae species has these states.

Cynolebias costai has one evident autapomorphy:

> (23) - Caudal fin of male hyaline. No other Cynolebiatinae species has this color pattern.

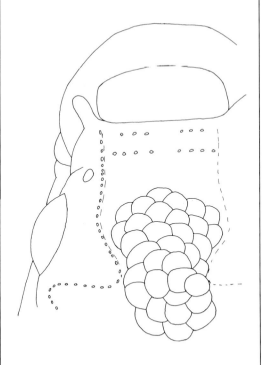

Fig. 40. Diagrammatic representation of dorsal view of head of *Cynolebias perforatus.*

Species of the "*C. elongatus* complex," *C. griseus,* and species of the "*C. porosus* complex" share five synapomorphies:

> (24) - Thirty-three or more vertebrae. All other Cynolebiatinae species have 31 or less vertebrae.
>
> (25) - Frontal squamation composed of about 20 irregularly distributed small scales. In other species of *Cynolebias* and related genera, frontal squamation comprises four or five principal scales (Fig. 40).
>
> (26) - Twenty-four to 39 neuromasts in supraorbital series. In other Rivulidae, supraorbital series is composed of six to 22 neuromasts.
>
> (27) - Upper pectoral radial absent (see synapomorphies of the "*C. bellottii* complex").
>
> (28) - Male reaching 80-120 mm SL. In any other Cynolebiatinae

males reach a length of 75 mm SL or less.

Cynolebias griseus and species of the "*C. porosus* complex" share one synapomorphy:

(29) - Male with dark blotches on posterodorsal region of head sides. No other species of *Cynolebias* and closely related genera has this color pattern.

Key to the Species of *Cynolebias*

1. - Frontal squamation composed of about 20 irregularly distributed small scales; 24-39 neuromasts in supraorbital series; male reaching 80-120 mm SL 26
   - Frontal squamation composed of four or five regularly distributed scales; 12-22 neuromasts in supraorbital series; male reaching 25-75 mm SL 2
2. - Head length of male 30% SL or more; anal fin of female hyaline; origin of dorsal fin of male opposite anal fin rays 1-5 or in front of anal fin origin 5
   - Head length of male 25% SL or less; anal fin of female reddish; origin of dorsal fin of male opposite anal fin rays 7-8 3
3. - Pectoral fin of male pointed, without papillae in inner surface, hyaline; no stripe on distal edge of anal fin of male 4
   - Pectoral fin of male rounded, with large papillae in inner surface, bluish with orange edge; male with orange stripe with golden reflections in distal edge of anal fin .... *C. whitei*
4. - Unpaired fins of male with dark transverse stripes and without dots; body depth of male about 25% SL .. .. *C. myersi*
   - Unpaired fins of male without stripes; dorsal and upper part of caudal fin of male with white dots; body depth of male about 30% SL .... *C. bokermanni*

5. - Length of dorsal fin of male 35-50% SL (except in *C. zonatus*); color pattern of male never of longitudinal rows of black blotches on body sides; eye diameter of male 35% HL or less 6
   - Length of dorsal fin of male about 30% SL; male with longitudinal rows of black blotches on body sides; eye diameter of male about 40% HL .... *C. constanciae*
6. - Five pelvic fin rays or no pelvic fin; never filamentous rays in dorsal fin of male 12
   - Six pelvic fin rays; male with or without filamentous rays in dorsal fin 7
7. - Male reaching about 40 mm SL; origin of dorsal fin behind anal fin origin 10
   - Male reaching about 30 mm SL; origin of dorsal fin in front of anal fin origin 8
8. - Caudal fin of male with bars; dorsal region of head with red scale edges; male without black blotch on body sides and without blue dots on sides and fins; origin of anal fin opposite dorsal fin rays 1-2 9
   - Caudal fin of male without bars; dorsal region of head of male without red scale edges; male with black blotch on center of body sides and with blue dots on sides, dorsal fin, and upper part of caudal fin; origin of anal fin opposite dorsal fin rays 3-4 .... *C. notatus*
9. - Male with long filamentous rays in dorsal fin; 21-22 dorsal fin rays in male .... *C. flammeus*
   - No filamentous rays in dorsal fin of male; 23-24 dorsal fin rays in male .... *C. magnificus*
10. - Male with 22-24 anal fin rays; origin of dorsal fin of male opposite dorsal fin rays 1-2; anal fin of male with dark distal edge 11
   - Male with 26 anal fin rays; origin of dorsal fin of male opposite dorsal fin rays 3-4; no dark distal edge in anal

fin of male .... *C. chacoensis*

11. - Sides of body of male with dark bars and without bright blue dots; caudal fin of male yellow .... *C. flavicaudatus*
    - Sides of body of male without dark bars and with white dots; caudal fin of male dark bluish gray . *C. antenori*

12. - Male never with five red bars on head sides; pelvic fin of male reaching anal fin 14
    - Male with five red bars on head sides; pelvic fin of male, when present, not reaching anal fin origin 13

13. - No pelvic fin; dorsal fin origin in front of anal fin origin; anal fin base smaller than dorsal fin base; 21-23 dorsal fin rays in male .... *C. boitonei*
    - Pelvic fin present; dorsal fin origin behind anal fin origin; anal fin base longer than dorsal fin base; 15-17 dorsal fin rays in male ... *C. zonatus*

14. - 26-37 scales in longitudinal series; caudal fin of male never hyaline; male reaching 30.0-75.0 mm SL . 15
    - 23-25 scales in longitudinal series; caudal fin of male hyaline; male reaching 25.0 mm SL .... *C. costai*

15. - Origin of dorsal fin behind anal fin origin 21
    - Origin of dorsal fin in front of anal fin origin 16

16. - Predorsal length of male 50% SL or less; length of dorsal fin base of male 45% SL or more 17
    - Predorsal length of male 55% SL or more; length of dorsal fin base of male about 35% SL ...... *C. carvalhoi*

17. - Adult male with body sides predominantly dark bluish gray 19
    - Sides of body of male yellowish green with dark bars 18

18. - No bars in anterior region of body sides of male; dark bars on sides of male without orange edges .... *C. luteoflammulatus*
    - Male with bars in anterior region of body sides; dark bars on sides of male with orange edges ....

.... *C. alexandri*

19. - Body depth of adult male about 30% SL 20
    - Body depth of adult male about 40% SL .... *C. affinis*

20. - Male with subdistal golden stripe in dorsal fin; no bars on body sides; scales present in preopercular region and on belly ..... *C. nigripinnis*
    - Male without stripes in dorsal fin and with light bars on body sides; no scales in preopercular region or on belly .... *C. gymnoventris*

21. - Length of anal fin of male 45-50% SL; body depth of male about 35% SL 23
    - Length of anal fin of male about 40% SL; body depth of male about 35% SL 22

22. - Female with distinctive black spots on caudal fin base; adult male reaching about 75 mm SL .... *C. nonoiuliensis*
    - No black spots on caudal fin base of female; adult male reaching about 40 mm SL .... *C. cinereus*

23. - Male with 23-26 anal fin rays; dark bars present on body sides 24
    - Male with 28-33 anal fin rays; no dark bars on body sides of male .... *C. bellottii*

24. - Posterior margin of pectoral fin of male reaching to anal fin rays 6-7; no black blotch on body sides of male; pectoral fin of male with black lower margin 25
    - Posterior margin of pectoral fin of male reaching to base of anal fin rays 2-3; male with blotch on center of body sides; pectoral fin of male hyaline .... *C. viarius*

25. - No spots on caudal fin base of male; urogenital papilla of male connected to anal fin .... *C. melanoorus*
    - Male with black spots on caudal fin base; urogenital papilla of male not connected to anal fin .... *C. adloffi*

26. - Dorsal fin of male pointed; male with dark blotches on posterodorsal region of head sides 30

- Dorsal fin of male rounded to somewhat pointed; no blotches on head sides of male 27

27. - Male with 23-26 anal fin rays; no dark bars on body sides of male .. 28
    - Male with 20-22 anal fin rays; dark bars on body sides of male .... *C. cheradophilus*

28. - Body sides of male dark bluish brown with bright gray dots over unpaired fins; lower jaw moderate 29
    - Body sides of male brown with bright yellowish brown blotches; lower jaw elongated ... *C. prognathus*

29. - Body depth of male about 35% SL; adult male with about 35 scales in longitudinal series .... *C. wolterstorffi*
    - Body depth of male about 30% SL; adult male with about 50 scales in longitudinal series .... *C. elongatus*

30. - Origin of dorsal fin behind anal fin origin; anal fin of male with filamentous rays 31
    - Origin of dorsal fin in front of anal fin origin; no filamentous rays in anal fin of male .... *C. griseus*

31. - Eye diameter of adult male (specimens larger than 75 mm SL) 19.4-23.0% SL; unpaired fins of male with light dots 32
    - Eye diameter of adult male (specimens larger than 75 mm SL) 15.4-17.2% SL; no dots on unpaired fins of male .... *C. microphthalmus*

32. - Adult male with 22-33 neuromasts in supraorbital, 27-31 in infraorbital, and 22-31 in preopercular series; distance between supraorbital series of neuromasts 19.5-23.0% HL in male 33
    - Adult male with 35-39 neuromasts in supraorbital, 35-36 in infraorbital, and 37-38 in preopercular series; distance between supraorbital series of neuromasts 12.0-15.0% HL in male ...... *C. perforatus*

33. - Length of anal fin base of adult male (specimens larger than 75 mm SL) 35.0-37.0% SL; body sides and unpaired fins of male dark brown with bright white dots .... *C. albipunctatus*
    - Length of anal fin base of adult male (specimens larger than 75 mm SL) 31.0-33.0% SL; body sides and unpaired fins of male brownish gray with pale gray dots .... *C. porosus*

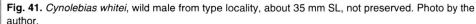

Fig. 41. *Cynolebias whitei*, wild male from type locality, about 35 mm SL, not preserved. Photo by the author.

Fig. 42 (above). *Cynolebias whitei*, wild male from type locality, about 45 mm SL, not preserved. Photo by the author.
Fig. 43 (below). *Cynolebias whitei*, wild male from type locality, about 45 mm SL, not preserved. Photo by the author.

Cynolebias whitei Myers
(Figs. 41-43)

Cynolebias whitei Myers, 1942:106 (original description; swamp near Cabo Frio, Rio de Janeiro, Brazil).
Pterolebias elegans Ladiges, 1958:76 (original description, Cabo Frio, Rio de Janeiro, Brazil).

Diagnosis.- Frontal squamation composed of four or five regularly distributed scales; about 15 neuromasts on supraorbital series; male reaching about 50 mm SL; head length of male about 25% SL; pectoral fin of male bluish with orange edge, rounded, and with large papillae on inner surface; caudal fin rounded; male with orange stripe with golden striae on distal edge of anal fin; anal fin of female reddish.

Description.- Dorsal and anal fins pointed in male, rounded in female. Caudal fin rounded. Short filamentous rays in dorsal fin of male. Pectoral fin rounded and with large papillae on inner surface. Posterior margin of pectoral fin reaches to base of seventh anal fin ray in male and to second anal fin ray in female. Pelvic fin reaches to base of third anal fin ray in male and to first anal fin ray in female. Origin of dorsal fin opposite anal fin rays 7-8 in male and anal fin rays 5-6 in female. Six pelvic fin rays. Head length of male about 25% SL. Frontal squamation composed of four or five regularly distributed scales. About 15 neuromasts in supraorbital series. Male reaching about 50 mm SL.

Coloration.- Male: sides of body and unpaired fins dark purplish brown with blue dots and striae. Orange stripe with golden striae on distal edge of anal fin. Pectoral fin bluish with golden striae and brownish orange stripe on margin. *Female*: sides of body pale brown with dark blotches and bars. Dorsal and caudal fins hyaline with dark spots. Anal fin reddish with dark spots.

Distribution.- Coastal plains between Rio das Ostras and Inoã, Rio de Janeiro, southeastern Brazil.

Fig. 44. *Cynolebias myersi*, wild male from Mucuri, about 30 mm SL, not preserved. Photo by G. Brasil.

Fig. 45. *Cynolebias myersi*, aquarium fish. Photo by K. Tanaka.

Cynolebias myersi Carvalho
(Figs. 44-48)

Cynolebias myersi Carvalho, 1971:401
   (original description; temporary pool
   near Conceição da Barra, Espírito
   Santo, Brazil).
Cynolebias izecksohni Cruz, 1983:74
   (original description; swamp near
   Linhares, Espírito Santo, Brazil). New
   synonymy.

Diagnosis.- Frontal squamation
composed of four or five regularly
distributed scales; about 15
neuromasts on supraorbital series;
male reaching about 40 mm SL; head
length of male about 25% SL; pectoral
fin of male hyaline, pointed, without
papillae; caudal fin pointed; no stripe
on distal edge of anal fin; anal fin of
female reddish; unpaired fins of male
with dark transverse stripes; body
depth of male about
25% SL.

Description.-
Dorsal and anal fins
pointed in male,
rounded in female.
Caudal fin pointed.
Short filamentous
rays in dorsal fin of
male. Pectoral fin
pointed, without
papillae. Posterior

margin of pectoral
fin reaches to base
of anal fin rays 7-8
in male and to anal
fin rays 5-6 in
female. Pelvic fin
reaches to base of
anal fin rays 2-3.
Origin of dorsal fin
opposite eighth
anal fin ray in male
and sixth anal fin
ray in female. Six
pelvic fin rays.
Head length of male
about 25% SL. Body depth of male
about 25% SL. Frontal squamation
composed of four or five regularly
distributed scales. About 15
neuromasts on supraorbital series.
Male reaching about 40 mm SL.

Coloration.- Male: body sides and
unpaired fins bluish green with
transverse crimson bars. Pectoral fin
hyaline. *Female*: sides of body brown
with dark bars. Dorsal and caudal fins
hyaline with dark spots. Anal fin pale
red with dark spots.

Distribution.- Coastal plains between
Prado, Bahia, and Linhares, Espírito
Santo, eastern Brazil.

Remarks.- Cynolebias izecksohni was
distinguished from *C. myersi* by having
a lanceolate caudal fin in both sexes
(vs. lanceolate only in female), more
bars in caudal fin (about nine in *C.
izecksohni* vs. about five in *C. myersi*)
and smaller head depth (Cruz, 1983).

Fig. 46. *Cynolebias myersi*, aquarium fish. Photo by K. Tanaka.

Fig. 47 (above). *Cynolebias myersi*, wild male from Linhares, the type locality of *C. izecksohni*, about 40 mm SL, not preserved. Photo by the author.

Fig. 48 (below). *Cynolebias myersi*, wild male from Prado, about 40 mm SL, not preserved. Photo by the author.

However, during the present study, based on samples from several additional localities, I could observe that the caudal fin of the males is always lanceolate, that the number of bars on the caudal fin is very variable, and that there is no difference in the head depth. Therefore, *C. izecksohni* is indistinguishable from *C. myersi* and must be considered as the same species.

Fig. 49. *Cynolebias bokermanni*, wild male from type locality, about 35 mm SL, not preserved. Photo by the author.

Cynolebias bokermanni Carvalho & Cruz
(Figs. 49-52)

Cynolebias bokermanni Carvalho & Cruz, 1987:12 (original description; swamp near Ilhéus, Bahia, Brazil).

Diagnosis.- Frontal squamation composed of four or five regularly distributed scales; about 15 neuromasts on supraorbital series; male reaching about 40 mm SL; head length of male about 25% SL; pectoral fin of male hyaline, pointed, and without papillae; caudal fin pointed; no stripe on distal edge of anal fin; anal fin of female reddish; dorsal and anal fins of male with white dots; body depth of male about 30% SL.

Description.- Dorsal and anal fins pointed in male, rounded in female. Caudal fin pointed. Short filamentous rays in dorsal fin of male. Pectoral fin pointed, without papillae. Posterior margin of pectoral fin reaches to base of anal fin rays 4-5 in male and to urogenital papillae in female. Pelvic fin reaches to base of anal fin rays 1-2 in male and to urogenital papillae in female. Origin of dorsal fin opposite eighth anal fin ray in male and fifth anal fin ray in female. Six pelvic fin rays. Head length of male about 25% SL. Body depth of male about 30% SL. Frontal squamation composed of four or five regularly distributed scales. About 15 neuromasts on supraorbital series. Male reaching about 40 mm SL.

Coloration.- *Male*: sides of body pale bluish green with faint purple bars and blue to white dots in dorsal region. Unpaired fins pale purple with blue to white dots on

Fig. 50. *Cynolebias bokermanni*, aquarium fish. Photo by Tanaka.

Fig. 51 (above). *Cynolebias bokermanni*, wild male from type locality, about 35 mm SL, not preserved. Photo by G. Brasil.

Fig. 52 (below). *Cynolebias bokermanni*, wild female from type locality, about 30 mm SL, not preserved. Photo by G. Brasil.

dorsal and caudal fins. Pectoral fin hyaline. *Female*: sides of body pale brown with dark blotches. Dorsal and caudal fins hyaline with dark spots. Anal fin pale red with dark spots.

Distribution.- Coastal plains near Ilhéus, Bahia, eastern Brazil.

Cynolebias constanciae Myers
(Figs. 53-56)

Cynolebias constanciae Myers, 1942:105 (original description; swamp near Cabo Frio, Rio de Janeiro, Brazil).

Diagnosis.- Frontal squamation composed of four or five regularly distributed scales; about 15 neuromasts on supraorbital series; male reaching about 40 mm SL; head length of male about 30% SL; length of dorsal fin base of male about 30% SL; male with four longitudinal rows of black blotches on body sides; eye diameter of male about 40% HL; male with long filamentous rays on dorsal fin surpassing end of caudal fin.

Description.- Dorsal and anal fins pointed in male, rounded in female. Caudal fin elliptical. Male with long filamentous rays on dorsal fin surpassing end of caudal fin. Pectoral fin rounded. Posterior margin of pectoral fin reaches to base of fifth anal fin ray in male and to second anal fin ray in female. Pelvic fin reaches to base of anal fin rays 2-3 in male and to first anal fin ray in female. Origin of dorsal fin opposite fifth anal fin ray in male and third anal fin ray in female. Six pelvic fin rays. Head length of male about 30% SL. Length of dorsal fin base of male about 30% SL. Eye diameter of male about 40% HL. Frontal squamation composed of four or five regularly distributed scales. About 15 neuromasts on supraorbital series. Male reaching about 40 mm SL.

Fig. 53. *Cynolebias constanciae*, wild male from type locality, about 30 mm SL, not preserved. Photo by the author.

Fig. 54 (above). *Cynolebias constanciae*, wild male from type locality, about 35 mm SL, not preserved. Photo by the author. **Fig. 55 (below).** *Cynolebias constanciae*, aquarium fish. Photo by E. Taylor. **Fig. 56 (bottom).** *Cynolebias constanciae*, aquarium fish. Photo by E. Taylor.

Coloration.- Male: sides of body slightly golden with four longitudinal rows of black blotches. Unpaired fins hyaline with black spots and golden reflections. *Female*: sides of body pale brown with dark blotches. Unpaired fins hyaline with dark spots.

Distribution.- Coastal plain near Cabo Frio, Rio de Janeiro, southern Brazil.

Remarks.- This species has been designated as a species threatened with extinction. In fact, the only locality where this fish was collected in recent years is being destroyed.

Cynolebias notatus
Costa, Lacerda & Brasil
(Figs. 57-58)

Cynolebias notatus Costa, Lacerda &
  Brasil, 1990:10 (original description;
  temporary lagoon, Alvorada do Norte,
  Goiás, Brazil).

Diagnosis.- Frontal squamation
composed of four or five regularly
distributed scales; about 15
neuromasts on supraorbital series;
male reaching about 30 mm SL; head
length of male about 30% SL; length of
dorsal fin base of male about 35% SL;
no filamentous rays in dorsal fin;
predorsal length of male about 50%
SL; six pelvic fin rays; origin of anal fin
of male opposite dorsal fin rays 3-4;
male with blue dots on dorsal region of
body, dorsal fin, and upper region of
caudal fin, and a black blotch on
center of body sides.

Description.- Dorsal and anal fins
pointed in male, rounded in female.
Caudal fin rounded. No filamentous
rays on dorsal fin. Pectoral fin
rounded. Posterior margin of pectoral
fin reaches to base of anal fin rays 5-7
in male and to urogenital papillae in
female. Pelvic fin reaches to base of
anal fin rays 1-2 in male and to
urogenital papillae in female. Origin of
anal fin opposite dorsal fin rays 3-4.
Six pelvic fin rays. Head length of male
about 30% SL. Length of dorsal fin
base of male about 35% SL. Predorsal
length of male about 50% SL. Frontal
squamation composed of four or five
regularly distributed scales. About 15
neuromasts on supraorbital series.
Male reaching about 30 mm SL.

Coloration.- Male: sides of body pale
brown with faint dark brown bars,
blue dots, and a black blotch in
center. Dorsal fin reddish brown with
dots, distal margin blue. Caudal fin

Fig. 57. *Cynolebias notatus*, wild male from type locality, about 25 mm SL, not preserved. Photo by G. Brasil.

Fig. 58. *Cynolebias notatus*, wild female from type locality, about 20 mm SL, not preserved. Photo by G. Brasil.

reddish brown with blue spots, upper margin blue. Anal fin reddish brown with faint dark brown bars. *Female*: sides of body pale brown with dark blotches. Unpaired fins hyaline with dark spots.

Distribution.- Rio Paranã basin, Goiás, central Brazil.

Cynolebias flammeus Costa
(Figs. 59-61)

Cynolebias flammeus Costa, 1990:185 (original description; swamp near the confluence of the Rio Bezerra with Rio Paranã, Tocantins, Brazil).

Diagnosis.- Frontal squamation composed of four or five regularly distributed scales; about 15 neuromasts on supraorbital series; male reaching about 30 mm SL; head length of male about 30% SL; length of dorsal fin base of male about 35% SL; long filamentous rays in dorsal fin of male; predorsal length of male about 50% SL; six pelvic fin rays; origin of anal fin of male opposite dorsal fin rays 1-2; caudal fin of male with bars; dorsal region of head of male with red edged scales.

Description.- Dorsal and anal fins pointed in male, rounded in female. Caudal fin somewhat truncate. Long filamentous rays in dorsal fin of male. Pectoral fin rounded. Posterior margin of pectoral fin reaches to base of anal fin rays 7-9 in male and to first anal fin ray in female. Pelvic fin reaches base of anal fin rays 1-3 in male and urogenital papillae in female. Origin of anal fin opposite dorsal fin rays 1-2. Six pelvic fin rays. Head length of male about 30% SL. Length of dorsal fin base of male about 35% SL. Predorsal length of male about 50% SL. Frontal squamation composed of four or five regularly distributed scales. About 15 neuromasts on supraorbital series. Male reaching about 30 mm SL.

Coloration.- Male: sides of body and unpaired fins bright blue with pale

Fig. 59 (above). *Cynolebias flammeus*, wild male from Nova Roma, about 25 mm SL, not preserved. Photo by G. Brasil.
Fig. 60 (below). *Cynolebias flammeus*, wild male from Nova Roma, about 25 mm SL, not preserved. Photo by G. Brasil.

Fig. 61. *Cynolebias flammeus*, wild female from Nova Roma, about 20 mm SL, not preserved. Photo by G. Brasil.

crimson bars. Dorsal region of head bright blue with red edged scales. *Female*: sides of body pale brown with dark spots. Unpaired fins hyaline.

Distribution.- Rio Paraná basin, Tocantins, and Goiás, central Brazil.

Cynolebias magnificus Costa & Brasil
(Figs. 62-63)

Cynolebias magnificus Costa & Brasil, 1991:59 (original description; temporary puddle, Manga, Minas Gerais, Brazil).

Diagnosis.- Frontal squamation composed of four or five regularly distributed scales; about 15 neuromasts on supraorbital series; male reaching about 30 mm SL; head length of male about 30% SL; length of dorsal fin base of male about 40% SL; no filamentous rays on dorsal fin of male; predorsal length of male about 50% SL; six pelvic fin rays; origin of anal fin of male opposite dorsal fin rays 1-2; caudal fin of male with bars; dorsal region of head of male with red edged scales.

Description.- Dorsal and anal fins pointed in male, rounded in female. Caudal fin rounded. No filamentous rays on dorsal fin. Pectoral fin rounded. Posterior margin of pectoral fin reaches to base of anal fin rays 6-7 in male and to anal fin rays 1-2 in female. Pelvic fin reaches to base of anal fin rays 2-3. Origin of anal fin opposite dorsal fin rays 1-2. Six pelvic fin rays. Head length of male about 30% SL. Length of dorsal fin base of male about 40% SL. Predorsal length of male about 50% SL. Frontal squamation composed of four or five regularly distributed scales. About 15 neuromasts on supraorbital series. Male reaching about 30 mm SL.

Coloration.- Male: sides of body predominantly purple with green anterior part and red dorsal region;

Fig. 62 (above). *Cynolebias magnificus*, wild male from type locality, about 25 mm SL, not preserved. Photo by G. Brasil.
Fig. 63 (below). *Cynolebias magnificus*, wild female from type locality, about 20 mm SL, not preserved. Photo by G. Brasil.

blue dots over body sides, except in anteroventral region, and two or three faint red bars in anterior body. Unpaired fins red with transverse rows of greenish blue stripes. *Female*: sides of body brown with dark bars and spots. Unpaired fins hyaline.

Distribution.- Middle São Francisco basin, Minas Gerais, central Brazil.

Cynolebias chacoensis Amato

Cynolebias chacoensis Amato, 1986:10 (original description; Monos flood plains, Nueva Asunción, Paraguay).

Diagnosis.- Frontal squamation composed of four or five regularly distributed scales; about 15 neuromasts on supraorbital series; male reaching about 40 mm SL; head length of male about 30% SL; length of dorsal fin base of male about 40% SL; long filamentous rays on dorsal fin of male; predorsal length of male about 45% SL; six pelvic fin rays; origin of dorsal fin of male opposite anal fin rays 3-4; 26 anal fin rays in male.

Description.- Dorsal fin pointed. Anal fin pointed in male, rounded in female. Caudal fin rounded. Long filamentous rays on dorsal fin of male. Pectoral fin rounded. Posterior margin of pectoral fin reaches to base of anal fin rays 7-8 in male and to first anal ray in female. Pelvic fin reaches to base of first anal fin ray. Origin of dorsal fin opposite anal fin rays 1-2. Six pelvic fin rays. Twenty-six anal fin rays in male. Head length of male about 30% SL. Length of dorsal fin base of male about 40% SL. Predorsal length of male about 50% SL. Frontal squamation composed of four or five regularly distributed scales. About 15 neuromasts on supraorbital series. Male reaching about 40 mm SL.

Coloration.- Male: sides of body and unpaired fins bluish gray with bright blue dots. *Female*: sides of body pale brown with dark bars and spots. Unpaired fins hyaline with dark spots.

Distribution.- Middle Paraguay basin, Nueva Asunción, Paraguay.

Cynolebias flavicaudatus Costa & Brasil
(Figs. 64-66)

Cynolebias flavicaudatus Costa & Brasil, 1990:18 (original description; temporary flooded area near Lagoa Grande, Santa Maria da Boa Vista, Pernambuco, Brazil).

Diagnosis.- Frontal squamation composed of four or five regularly distributed scales; about 15 neuromasts on supraorbital series; male reaching about 40 mm SL; head length of male about 30% SL; length of dorsal fin base of male about 40% SL; long filamentous rays in dorsal fin of male; predorsal length of male about 45% SL; six pelvic fin rays; origin of dorsal fin of male opposite anal fin rays 1-2; 22-24 anal fin rays in male; male with caudal fin and posterior areas of dorsal and anal fins yellow, anterior areas of dorsal and anal fins pale purplish red, and blue dots over dorsal and anal fins as well as in posterior area of anal fin; body sides of both sexes with dark bars.

Description.- Dorsal and anal fins pointed in male, rounded in female. Caudal fin somewhat truncate. Long filamentous rays in dorsal fin of male. Pectoral fin rounded. Posterior margin of pectoral fin reaches to base of anal fin rays 5-6 in male and to anal fin rays 1-2 in female. Pelvic fin reaches to base of third anal fin ray in male and to urogenital papillae or first anal fin ray in female. Origin of dorsal fin opposite anal fin rays 1-2 in male and anal fin rays 3-4 in female. Six pelvic fin rays. Twenty-two to 24 anal fin rays in male. Head length of male about 30% SL. Length of dorsal fin base of male about 40% SL. Predorsal length of male about

Fig. 64 (above). *Cynolebias flavicaudatus*, wild male from type locality, about 40 mm SL, not preserved. Photo by G. Brasil.
Fig. 65 (below). *Cynolebias flavicaudatus*, wild female from type locality, about 35 mm SL, not preserved. Photo by G. Brasil.

Fig. 66. *Cynolebias flavicaudatus*, wild male from Januaria, about 40 mm SL, not preserved. Photo by G. Brasil.

50% SL. Frontal squamation composed of four or five regularly distributed scales. About 15 neuromasts on supraorbital series. Male reaching about 40 mm SL.

Coloration.- Male: sides of body purplish gray with dark gray bars. Caudal fin and posterior areas of dorsal and anal fins yellow; anterior areas of dorsal and anal fins pale purplish red; blue dots over dorsal and anal fins as well as in posterior area of anal fin; anal fin with black stripe on distal edge adjacent to subdistal orange stripe. *Female*: sides of body pale brown with dark bars and spots. Unpaired fins hyaline.

Distribution.- Middle Rio São Francisco basin, between Lagoa Grande, Pernambuco, and Januária, Minas Gerais, northeastern Brazil.

Cynolebias antenori Tulipano
(Fig. 67)

Cynolebias antenori Myers, 1952:139 (nomem nudum).
Cynolebias antenori Tulipano, 1973:23 (original description; Ceará, Brazil).
Cynolebias heloplites Huber, 1981:1 (original description; lagoon between Fortaleza and Russas, Ceará, Brazil).

Diagnosis.- Frontal squamation composed of four or five regularly distributed scales; about 15 neuromasts on supraorbital series; male reaching about 40 mm SL; head length of male about 30% SL; length of dorsal fin base of male about 40% SL; long filamentous rays in dorsal fin of male; predorsal length of male about 45% SL; six pelvic fin rays; origin of dorsal fin of male opposite anal fin rays 1-2; 22-24 anal fin rays in male; unpaired fins of male dark bluish gray with white dots; male with white dots over body sides and faint bars on anterior region; no bars on body sides of female.

Description.- Dorsal and anal fins pointed in male, rounded in female. Caudal fin somewhat truncate. Long filamentous rays on dorsal fin of male. Pectoral fin rounded. Posterior margin

Fig. 67. *Cynolebias antenori*, male, aquarium fish. Photo by E. Taylor.

of pectoral fin reaches to base of anal fin rays 5-6 in male and to anal fin rays 1-2 in female. Pelvic fin reaches to base of third anal fin ray in male and to urogenital papilla or first anal fin ray in female. Origin of dorsal fin opposite anal fin rays 1-2 in male and anal fin rays 3-4 in female. Six pelvic fin rays. Twenty-two to 24 anal fin rays in male. Head length of male about 30% SL. Length of dorsal fin base of male about 40% SL. Predorsal length of male about 50% SL. Frontal squamation composed of four or five regularly distributed scales. About 15 neuromasts on supraorbital series. Male reaching about 40 mm SL.

Coloration.- *Male*: sides of body brown with faint bars on anterior region and white dots over body sides. Unpaired fins dark bluish gray with white dots. Anal fin with black stripe on distal edge adjacent to subdistal orange stripe. *Female*: sides of body pale brown with dark blotches. Unpaired fins hyaline.

Distribution.- Coastal plains between Pacajús, Ceará and Mossoró, Rio Grande do Norte, northeastern Brazil.

Cynolebias zonatus Costa & Brasil
(Figs. 68-69)

Cynolebias zonatus Costa & Brasil, 1990:16 (original description;

temporary puddle near Garapuava, Unaí, Minas Gerais, Brazil).

Diagnosis.- Frontal squamation composed of four or five regularly distributed scales; about 15 neuromasts on supraorbital series; male reaching about 30 mm SL; head length of male about 30% SL; length of dorsal fin base of male about 25% SL; no filamentous rays on dorsal fin of male; longest dorsal fin ray of male equal to length of dorsal fin base; five pelvic fin rays; reduced pelvic fin; male with four red bars on sides of head and black spots in basal region of dorsal fin; dorsal fin origin behind anal fin origin; anal fin base of male longer than dorsal fin base; 15-17 dorsal fin rays in male.

Description.- Dorsal and anal fins pointed in male, rounded in female. Caudal fin rounded. No filamentous rays on dorsal fin of male. Pectoral fin rounded. Posterior margin of pectoral fin reaches to base of anal fin rays 4-6 in male and to urogenital papilla in female. Pelvic fin reduced, reaching to urogenital papilla in male and to anus in female. Five pelvic fin rays. Origin of dorsal fin opposite anal fin rays 3-4 in male and second anal fin ray in female. Six pelvic fin rays. Head length of male about 30% SL. Length of dorsal fin base of male about 25% SL. Longest dorsal fin ray of

Fig. 68 (above). *Cynolebias zonatus*, wild male from type locality, about 30 mm SL, not preserved. Photo by G. Brasil.

Fig. 69 (below). *Cynolebias zonatus*, wild female from type locality, about 25 mm SL, not preserved. Photo by G. Brasil.

Fig. 70. *Cynolebias boitonei*, male, aquarium fish. Photo by J. Kadlec.

male equal to length of dorsal fin base. Anal fin base of male longer than dorsal fin base. Fifteen to 17 dorsal fin rays in male. Frontal squamation composed of four or five regularly distributed scales. About 15 neuromasts on supraorbital series. Male reaching about 30 mm SL.

Coloration.- Male: sides of body blue with red bars, which are interconnected on caudal peduncle. Dorsal fin red with blue spots; black spots on basal region. Caudal fin red with blue spots. Anal fin orange with two horizontal rows of blue spots; distal edge red. Four red bars on sides of head, first crossing eye, second close to the posterior margin of orbit, and two on opercular region. *Female*: sides of body pale brown with dark bars and central black blotch. Dorsal and caudal fins hyaline. Anal fin yellowish.

Distribution.- Upper Rio São Francisco basin, Minas Gerais, central Brazil.

Cynolebias boitonei (Carvalho)
(Figs. 70-72)

Simpsonichthys boitonei Carvalho, 1959:5 (original description; temporary puddle in Brasília, Goiás (now Distrito Federal), Brazil).
Cynolebias boitonei; Peters & Seegers, 1978:390.

Diagnosis.- Frontal squamation composed of four or five regularly distributed scales; about 15 neuromasts on supraorbital series; male reaching about 40 mm SL; head length of male about 30% SL; length of dorsal fin base of male about 35% SL; no filamentous rays in dorsal fin of male; length of longest dorsal fin ray of male equal to length of dorsal fin base; pelvic fin absent; male with four red bars on sides of head and black spots

Fig. 71. *Cynolebias boitonei*, female, aquarium fish. Photo by J. Kadlec.

Fig. 72. *Cynolebias boitonei*, wild male from Brasilia, about 20 mm SL, not preserved. Photo by the author.

in basal region of dorsal fin; dorsal fin origin in front of anal fin origin; anal fin base of male shorter than dorsal fin base; 21-23 dorsal fin rays in male.

Description.- Dorsal and anal fins pointed in male, rounded in female. Caudal fin rounded. No filamentous rays in dorsal fin of male. Pectoral fin rounded. Posterior margin of pectoral fin reaches base of anal fin rays 4-5 in male and anus in female. Pelvic fin absent. Origin of anal fin opposite sixth dorsal fin ray in male and first anal fin ray in female. Head length of male about 30% SL. Length of dorsal fin base of male about 35% SL. Length of longest dorsal fin ray of male equal to length of dorsal fin base. Anal fin base of male shorter than dorsal fin base. Male with 21 to 23 dorsal fin rays. Frontal squamation composed of four or five regularly distributed scales. About 15 neuromasts in supraorbital series. Male reaching about 40 mm SL.

Coloration.- Male: sides of body blue with red bars, which are interconnected in caudal peduncle. Dorsal fin red with golden spots; black spots on basal region. Caudal fin reddish with blue spots and margins. Anal fin red with two or three rows of blue spots. Four red bars on sides of head: first crossing eye, second close to posterior margin of orbit, and two

on opercular region. *Female*: sides of body pale brown with dark bars and one to three central black blotches. Unpaired fins hyaline.

Distribution.- Rio São Francisco flood plains, upper Paraná basin, Distrito Federal, central Brazil.

Cynolebias costai Lazara
(Fig. 73)

Cynolebias costai Lazara, 1991:144 (original description; temporary pool in Aruanã, Goiás, Brazil).

Diagnosis.- Frontal squamation composed of four or five regularly distributed scales; about 14 neuromasts on supraorbital series; male reaching about 25 mm SL; head length of male about 30% SL; length of dorsal fin base of male about 35% SL; length of longest dorsal fin ray of male about 30% length of dorsal fin base; 23-25 scales in longitudinal series; caudal fin of male hyaline.

Description.- Dorsal and anal fins gently pointed in male, rounded in female. Caudal fin somewhat truncate. No filamentous rays in dorsal fin of male. Pectoral fin rounded. Posterior margin of pectoral fin reaches to base of anal fin rays 4-6 in male and to urogenital papilla in female. Pelvic fin reaches to base of

Fig. 73. *Cynolebias costai*, wild male from swamp near Rio das Mortes, about 20 mm SL, not preserved. Photo by G. Brasil.

first anal fin ray. Origin of dorsal fin opposite anal fin rays 3-4. Head length of male about 30% SL. Length of longest dorsal fin ray of male about 30% length of dorsal fin base. Twenty-three to 25 scales in longitudinal series. Frontal squamation composed of four or five regularly distributed scales. About 14 neuromasts on supraorbital series. Male reaching about 25 mm SL.

Coloration.- Male: sides of body dark brown with blue dots. Dorsal and anal fins dark brown with subdistal transverse bright blue stripes; bright blue dots in basal region. Caudal fin hyaline with pale blue posterior edge. *Female*: sides of body pale brown with dark brown and black blotches. Unpaired fins hyaline; gray dots in dorsal and anal fins.

Distribution.- Upper Araguaia and Rio das Mortes basins, Goiás and Mato Grosso, central Brazil.

Cynolebias carvalhoi Myers
(Fig. 74)

Cynolebias carvalhoi Myers, 1947:19 (original description; Rio Iguassú, near Porto União, Santa Catarina, Brazil).

Diagnosis.- Frontal squamation composed of four or five regularly distributed scales; about 20 neuromasts on supraorbital series; male reaching about 30 mm SL; head length of male about 35% SL; length of dorsal fin base of male about 35% SL; length of longest dorsal fin ray of male about 40% length of dorsal fin base; five pelvic fin rays; no filamentous rays in dorsal fin of male; anal fin origin behind dorsal fin origin; predorsal length of male about 55% SL.

Description.- Dorsal and anal fins pointed in male, rounded in female. Caudal fin somewhat truncate in male, rounded in female. No filamentous

Fig. 74. *Cynolebias carvalhoi*, paratype, male, 25 mm SL, MNRJ 5760.

rays in dorsal fin of male. Pectoral fin rounded. Posterior margin of pectoral fin reaches to base of anal fin rays 2-5 in male and to first anal fin ray in female. Pelvic fin reaches to base of first anal fin ray in male and to urogenital papilla in female. Origin of anal fin opposite dorsal fin rays 2-3. Five pelvic fin rays. Head length of male about 35% SL. Length of longest dorsal fin ray of male about 40% length of dorsal fin base. Predorsal length of male about 55%. Frontal squamation composed of four or five regularly distributed scales. About 20 neuromasts on supraorbital series. Male reaching about 30 mm SL.

Coloration (in alcohol).- Male: sides of body pale gray with 7-9 vertical dark bars. *Female*: sides of body pale gray with dark gray spots in whole extension; black spots in central region.

Distribution.- Upper Iguassú basin, Santa Catarina, southern Brazil.

Remarks.- This species has not been found since the type material was collected in 1944, although there were recent attempts to do so. It may be extinct.

Cynolebias luteoflammulatus Vaz-Ferreira, Soriano & Paulete

Cynolebias luteoflammulatus Vaz-Ferreira, Soriano & Paulete, 1964:25 (original description; temporary swamp near Arroyo Valizas, Rocha, Uruguay).

Diagnosis.- Frontal squamation composed of four or five regularly distributed scales; about 20 neuromasts on supraorbital series; male reaching about 40 mm SL; head length of male about 30% SL; length of dorsal fin base of male about 50% SL; length of longest dorsal fin ray of male about 30% length of dorsal fin base; five pelvic fin rays; no filamentous rays in dorsal fin of male; anal fin origin behind dorsal fin origin; predorsal length of male about 45% SL; body sides of adult male yellowish green with dark bars that are not present in anterior region of body.

Description.- Dorsal and anal fins somewhat pointed in male, rounded in female. Caudal fin rounded. No filamentous rays in dorsal fin of male. Pectoral fin rounded. Posterior margin of pectoral fin reaches to base of third anal fin ray in male and to pelvic fin base in female. Pelvic fin reaches to base of fourth anal fin ray in male and to second anal fin ray in female. Origin of anal fin opposite second dorsal fin ray. Five pelvic fin rays. Head length of male about 30% SL. Length of dorsal fin base of male about 50% SL. Length of longest dorsal fin ray of male about 30% length of dorsal fin base. Predorsal length of male about 45% SL. Frontal squamation composed of four or five regularly distributed scales. About 20 neuromasts on supraorbital series. Male reaching about 40 mm SL.

Coloration.- Male: sides of body yellowish green with dark bars in median and posterior regions of sides. Unpaired fins dark gray with green reflections and dots. *Female*: sides of body pale brown with dark brown blotches and bars. Fins hyaline with pale spots on basal region of unpaired fins.

Fig. 75. *Cynolebias alexandri*, paratype, male from Gualeguachu. Photo by H. P. Castello.

Distribution.- Lowlands of Rocha and Treinta y Tres, eastern Uruguay.

Cynolebias alexandri Castello & Lopez
(Figs. 75-77)

Cynolebias alexandri Castello & Lopez, 1974:35 (original description; Parque Unzue, Gualeguaychu, Entre Rios, Argentina).

Diagnosis.- Frontal squamation composed of four or five regularly distributed scales; about 20 neuromasts on supraorbital series; male reaching about 40 mm SL; head length of male about 30% SL; length of dorsal fin base of male about 50% SL; length of longest dorsal fin ray of male about 35% length of dorsal fin base; five pelvic fin rays; no filamentous rays in dorsal fin of male; anal fin origin behind dorsal fin origin; predorsal length of male about 45% SL; body sides of adult male yellowish green with orange-edged dark bars on entire body.

Description.- Dorsal and anal fins somewhat pointed in male, rounded in female. Caudal fin rounded. No filamentous rays in dorsal fin of male. Pectoral fin rounded. Posterior margin of pectoral fin reaches to base of sixth anal fin ray in male and to anus in

Fig. 76. *Cynolebias alexandri*, aquarium fish, albino specimen.

Fig. 77. *Cynolebias alexandri*, female, aquarium fish. Photo by HJ. Richter.

female. Pelvic fin reaches to base of fourth anal fin ray in male and to second anal fin ray in female. Origin of anal fin opposite dorsal fin rays 2-3. Five pelvic fin rays. Head length of male about 30% SL. Length of dorsal fin base of male about 50% SL. Length of the greatest dorsal fin ray of male about 35% length of dorsal fin base. Predorsal length of male about 45% SL. Body depth of male about 30% SL. Frontal squamation composed of four or five regularly distributed scales. About 20 neuromasts on supraorbital series. Male reaching about 40 mm SL.

Coloration.- *Male*: sides of body yellowish green with orange-edged dark bars on entire length of body. Unpaired fins dark bluish gray with blue dots. *Female*: sides of body pale brown with dark blotches. Unpaired fins hyaline with dark spots on basal region.

Distribution.- Rio Uruguay basin including northeastern Argentina, western Uruguay, and southern Brazil.

Cynolebias affinis Amato
(Figs. 78-80)

Cynolebias affinis Amato, 1986:6 (original description; Arroyo Tres Cruces basin, Tacuarembó,

Uruguay).
Cynolebias cyaneus Amato, 1987:2 (original description, Arroyo Dom Marcos basin, Rio Pardo, Rio Grande do Sul, Brazil), new synonymy.

Diagnosis.- Frontal squamation composed of four or five regularly distributed scales; about 20 neuromasts on supraorbital series; male reaching about 50 mm SL; head length of male about 30% SL; length of dorsal fin base of male about 50% SL; length of longest dorsal fin ray of male about 30% length of dorsal fin base; five pelvic fin rays; no filamentous rays in dorsal fin of male; anal fin origin behind dorsal fin origin; predorsal length of male about 50% SL; adult male with body sides predominantly dark bluish gray, without bars; body depth of male about 40% SL.

Description.- Dorsal and anal fins somewhat pointed in male, rounded in female. Caudal fin rounded. No filamentous rays in dorsal fin of male. Pectoral fin rounded. Posterior margin of pectoral fin reaches to base of anal fin rays 3-4 in male and to base of pelvic fin in female. Pelvic fin reaches to base of third anal fin ray in male and to urogenital papilla in female. Origin of anal fin opposite dorsal fin

Fig. 78 (above). *Cynolebias affinis*, wild male from type locality of *C. cyaneus*, about 35 mm SL, not preserved. Photo by G. Brasil.
Fig. 79 (below). *Cynolebias affinis*, aquarium fish. Photo by Kadlec.

Fig. 80. *Cynolebias affinis*, aquarium fish. Photo by J. Kadlec.

rays 2-3. Five pelvic fin rays. Head length of male about 30% SL. Length of dorsal fin base of male about 50% SL. Length of longest dorsal fin ray of male about 30% length of dorsal fin base. Predorsal length of male about 50% SL. Body depth of male about 40% SL. Frontal squamation composed of four or five regularly distributed scales. About 20 neuromasts on supraorbital series. Male reaching about 50 mm SL.

Coloration.- Male: sides of body and unpaired fins dark bluish gray with blue dots. *Female*: sides of body pale brown with dark blotches. Unpaired fins hyaline with dark spots.

Distribution.- Arroyo Tres Cruces Basin, Tacuarembó, northern Uruguay.

Remarks.–Amato (1987) pointed out two differences between *C. affinis* and *C. cyaneus*, the presence of darks bars on the body of adult males and the absence of bright spots on the anal fin

and lower part of the caudal fin of males of *C. cyaneus*. However, the examination of adult specimens collected in some swamps close to the type locality of *C. cyaneus* revealed that it is indistinguishable from *C. affinis*.

Cynolebias nigripinnis Regan
(Fig. 81)

Cynolebias nigripinnis Regan, 1912:508 (original description; La Plata, Argentina).

Diagnosis.- Frontal squamation composed of four or five regularly distributed scales; about 20 neuromasts on supraorbital series; male reaching about 40 mm SL; head length of male about 30% SL; length of dorsal fin base of male about 50% SL; length of longest dorsal fin ray of male about 40% length of dorsal fin base; five pelvic fin rays; no filamentous rays

Fig. 81. *Cynolebias nigripinnis*, male, aquarium fish. Photo by B. Kahl.

in dorsal fin of male; anal fin origin behind dorsal fin origin; predorsal length of male about 45% SL; adult male with body sides predominantly dark bluish gray, without bars; subdistal golden stripe on dorsal fin present; body depth of male about 30% SL.

Description.- Dorsal and anal fins somewhat pointed in male, rounded in female. Caudal fin rounded. No filamentous rays on dorsal fin of male. Pectoral fin rounded. Posterior margin of pectoral fin reaches to base of anal fin rays 3-4 in male and to base of pelvic fin in female. Pelvic fin reaches to base of fourth anal fin ray in male and to anal fin rays 1-2 in female. Origin of anal fin opposite dorsal fin rays 2-3. Five pelvic fin rays. Head length of male about 30% SL. Length of dorsal fin base of male about 50% SL. Length of longest dorsal fin ray of male about 30% length of dorsal fin base. Predorsal length of male about 45% SL. Body depth of male about 30% SL. Frontal squamation composed of four or five regularly distributed scales. About 20 neuromasts on supraorbital series. Male reaching about 40 mm SL.

Coloration.- Male: sides of body and unpaired fins dark bluish gray to black with blue spots; golden subdistal stripe on dorsal fin. *Female*: sides of body pale brown with dark brown blotches. Fins hyaline; pale spots on basal region of unpaired fins.

Distribution.- Lower Paraná and Uruguay basins, northeastern Argentina, and western Uruguay.

Cynolebias gymnoventris Amato
(Fig. 82)

Cynolebias gymnoventris Amato, 1986:2 (original description;Arroyo India Muerta basin, near Velázquez, Rocha, Uruguay).

Diagnosis.- Frontal squamation composed of four or five regularly distributed scales; about 20 neuromasts on supraorbital series; male reaching about 30 mm SL; head length of male about 30% SL; length of dorsal fin base of male about 50% SL; length of longest dorsal fin ray of male about 30% length of dorsal fin base; five pelvic fin rays; no filamentous rays in dorsal fin of male; anal fin origin behind dorsal fin origin; predorsal length of male about 50% SL; adult male with body sides predominantly dark bluish gray, with about six light bars; body depth of male about 30% SL; no scales on preopercular and anteroventral regions.

Description.- Dorsal and anal fins somewhat pointed in male, rounded in female. Caudal fin rounded. No filamentous rays on dorsal fin of male.

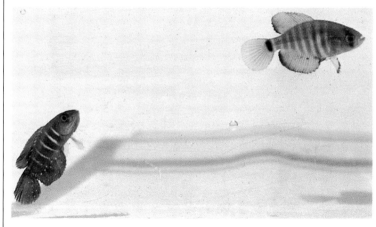

Fig. 82. *Cynolebias viarius*, male (left), and *C. gymnoventris*, male (right), aquarium fishes.

Pectoral fin rounded. Posterior margin of pectoral fin reaches to base of anal fin rays 2-3 in male and to base of pelvic fin in female. Pelvic fin reaches to base of anal fin rays 1-2. Origin of anal fin opposite dorsal fin rays 3-4. Five pelvic fin rays. Head length of male about 30% SL. Length of dorsal fin base of male about 50% SL. Length of longest dorsal fin ray of male about 30% length of dorsal fin base. Predorsal length of male about 50% SL. Body depth of male about 30% SL. Frontal squamation composed of four or five regularly distributed scales. About 20 neuromasts on supraorbital series. Male reaching approximately 30 mm SL.

Coloration.- Male: sides of body dark bluish gray with about five light bars. Unpaired fins dark bluish gray with blue spots. *Female*: sides of body brown with dark blotches. Unpaired fins hyaline with dark spots.

Distribution.- Lowlands between southern Rio Grande do Sul, southern Brazil, and Rocha, eastern Uruguay.

Cynolebias nonoiuliensis
Taberner, Santos & Castelli

Cynolebias nonoiuliensis Taberner, Santos & Castelli, 1974:187 (original description; temporary swamps, Nueve de Julio, Buenos Aires, Argentina).

Diagnosis.- Frontal squamation composed of four or five regularly distributed scales; about 20 neuromasts on supraorbital series; male reaching about 75 mm SL; head length of male about 30% SL; length of longest dorsal fin ray of male about 30% length of dorsal fin base; five pelvic fin rays; no filamentous rays in dorsal fin of male; anal fin origin in front of dorsal fin origin; body depth of male about 30% SL; female with distinctive black spots on caudal fin base.

Description.- Dorsal and anal fins rounded. Caudal fin rounded. No filamentous rays in dorsal fin of male. Pectoral fin rounded. Posterior margin of pectoral fin reaches to base of anal fin rays 4-6 in male and to anus in female. Pelvic fin reaches to base of anal fin rays 3-4 in male and to first anal fin ray in female. Origin of anal fin opposite dorsal fin rays 2-3. Five pelvic fin rays. Head length of male about 30% SL. Length of longest dorsal fin ray of male about 30% length of dorsal fin base. Body depth of male about 30% SL. Frontal squamation composed of four or five regularly distributed scales. About 20 neuromasts on supraorbital series. Male reaching about 75 mm SL.

Coloration.- Male: sides of body and unpaired fins dark bluish gray. *Female*: sides of body pale brown with blotches and bars. About three black spots on caudal fin base. Unpaired fins hyaline with dark spots.

Distribution.- Rio Salado basin, Buenos Aires, northeastern Argentina.

Cynolebias cinereus Amato
(Figs. 83-84)

Cynolebias carvalhoi (non *Cynolebias carvalhoi* Myers, 1947); Vaz-Ferreira & Sierra, 1971:30 (misidentification).
Cynolebias cinereus Amato, 1986:9 (original description; swamp near Arroyo de las Víboras, Colonia, Uruguay).

Diagnosis.- Frontal squamation composed of four or five regularly distributed scales; about 20 neuromasts on supraorbital series; male reaching about 40 mm SL; head length of male about 30% SL; length of longest dorsal fin ray of male about 30% length of dorsal fin base; five pelvic fin rays; no filamentous rays in dorsal fin of male; anal fin origin in front of dorsal fin origin; body depth of male about 30% SL.

Description.- Dorsal and anal fins rounded. Caudal fin rounded. No filamentous rays in dorsal fin of male. Pectoral fin rounded. Posterior margin of pectoral fin reaches to base of anal fin rays 4-6 in male and to anus in female. Pelvic fin reaches to base of anal fin rays 3-4 in male and to first anal fin ray in female. Origin of anal fin opposite dorsal fin rays 2-3. Five pelvic fin rays. Head length of male about 30% SL. Length of longest dorsal fin ray of male about 30% length of dorsal fin base. Body depth of male about 30% SL. Frontal squamation composed of four or five

Fig. 83. *Cynolebias cinereus*, wild male from type locality, about 30 mm SL. Photo by the author.

Fig. 84. *Cynolebias cinereus*, aquarium fish. Photo by Tanaka.

regularly distributed scales. About 20 neuromasts on supraorbital series. Male reaching about 40 mm SL.

Coloration.- Male: sides of body and unpaired fins dark gray with green reflections. *Female*: sides of body pale brown with dark blotches. Unpaired fins hyaline with dark spots.

Distribution.- Coastal plains near Colonia, southwestern Uruguay.

Cynolebias bellottii Steindachner
(Figs. 85-86)

Cynolebias bellottii Steindachner, 1881:98 (original description; La Plata, Argentina).
Cynolebias maculatus Steindachner, 1881:98 (original description; La Plata, Argentina).
Cynolebias gibberosus Berg, 1897:294 (original description; Cacharí, Partido de Azul, Argentina).
Cynolebias bellotti; Perugia, 1891:655 (misspelling).
Cynolebias belotti; Stansch, 1909:77 (misspelling).
Cynolebias belottii; Ahl, 1922:2 (misspelling).
Cynolebias belloti; Ladiges, 1934b:201 (misspelling).
Cynolebias irregularis Ahl, 1938:54 (original description; probably Argentina).

Diagnosis.- Frontal squamation composed of four or five regularly distributed scales; about 20 neuromasts on supraorbital series; male reaching about 70 mm SL; head length of male about 30% SL; length of longest dorsal fin ray of male about

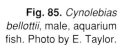

Fig. 85. *Cynolebias bellottii*, male, aquarium fish. Photo by E. Taylor.

Fig. 86. *Cynolebias bellottii*, female, aquarium fish. Dr. H. Castello.

30% length of dorsal fin base; five pelvic fin rays; no filamentous rays in dorsal fin of male; anal fin origin in front of dorsal fin origin; body depth of male about 45% SL; 28-33 anal fin rays in male; body sides of male with bright dots and without dark bars.

Description.- Dorsal and anal fins rounded. Caudal fin rounded to somewhat truncate. No filamentous rays in dorsal fin of male. Pectoral fin rounded. Posterior margin of pectoral fin reaches to base of second anal fin ray in male and to anus in female. Pelvic fin reaches to base of third anal fin ray in male and to first anal fin ray in female. Origin of dorsal fin opposite anal fin rays 2-3. Five pelvic fin rays. Twenty-eight to 33 anal fin rays in male. Head length of male about 30% SL. Length of longest dorsal fin ray of male about 30% length of dorsal fin base. Body depth of male about 45% SL. Frontal squamation composed of four or five regularly distributed scales. About 20 neuromasts on

supraorbital series. Male reaching about 70 mm SL.

Coloration.- Male: sides of body and unpaired fins dark blue with bright blue dots. *Female:* sides of body pale brown with dark blotches and bars. Unpaired fins hyaline with dark spots.

Distribution.- Rio Paraná, Rio Paraguay, Rio Uruguay, and Rio Salado basins, comprising Boqueron, western Paraguay, Salta, Formosa, Entre Rios, and Buenos Aires, northern and northeastern Argentina, and Artigas, Salto, Durazno, Soriano, and Colonia, western Uruguay.

Cynolebias viarius
Vaz-Ferreira, Soriano & Paulete
(Figs. 82, 87)

Cynolebias viarius Vaz-Ferreira, Soriano & Paulete, 1964:1 (original description; swamp between Arroyo Valizas and Balneario Aguas Dulces, Rocha, Uruguay).

Fig. 87. *Cynolebias viarius*, aquarium fish. Photo by K. Tanaka.

Diagnosis.- Frontal squamation composed of four or five regularly distributed scales; about 20 neuromasts on supraorbital series; male reaching about 60 mm SL; head length of male about 30% SL; length of longest dorsal fin ray of male about 45% length of dorsal fin base; five pelvic fin rays; no filamentous rays in dorsal fin of male; anal fin origin in front of dorsal fin origin; body depth of male about 45% SL; 21-26 anal fin rays in male; pectoral fin reaches to base of anal fin rays 2-3 in male; sides of body of male with about 10 bars; black spot in center of sides.

Description.- Dorsal and anal fins rounded. Caudal fin somewhat truncate. No filamentous rays in dorsal fin of male. Pectoral fin rounded. Posterior margin of pectoral fin reaches to base of anal fin rays 2-3 in male and to anus in female. Pelvic fin reaches to base of anal fin rays 3-4 in male and to first anal fin ray in female. Origin of dorsal fin opposite anal fin rays 4-5 in male and first anal fin ray in female. Five pelvic fin rays. Twenty-one to 26 anal fin rays in male. Head length of male about 30% SL. Length of longest dorsal fin ray of male about 45% length of dorsal fin base. Body depth of male about 45% SL. Frontal squamation composed of four or five regularly distributed scales.

About 20 neuromasts on supraorbital series. Male reaching about 60 mm SL.

Coloration.- Male: sides of body light greenish gray with about ten dark bars and a black spot in center of body. Dorsal fin pale brown with bright green dots. Caudal fin bluish. Anal fin dark with bright green dots. *Female*: sides of body pale brown with dark blotches and bars. Unpaired fins hyaline with dark spots.

Distribution.- Lowlands near Rocha, eastern Uruguay.

Cynolebias melanoorus Amato

Cynolebias melanoorus Amato, 1986:4 (original description; Arroyo Tres Cruces flood plains, Tacuarembó, Uruguay).

Diagnosis.- Frontal squamation composed of four or five regularly distributed scales; about 20 neuromasts on supraorbital series; male reaching about 40 mm SL; head length of male about 30% SL; length of longest dorsal fin ray of male about 30% length of dorsal fin base; five pelvic fin rays; no filamentous rays in dorsal fin of male; anal fin origin in front of dorsal fin origin; body depth of male about 40% SL; 23-27 anal fin rays in male; pectoral fin reaches to base of anal fin rays 2-3 in male; sides of body of male with about 20 bars; male with black margins on lower region of pectoral fin; urogenital papilla of male connected to anal fin.

Description.- Dorsal and anal fins somewhat pointed in male, rounded in female. Caudal fin rounded. No filamentous rays in dorsal fin of male. Pectoral fin rounded. Posterior margin of pectoral fin reaches to base of anal fin rays 2-3 in male and to anus in female. Pelvic fin reaches to base of anal fin rays 2-3 in male and to anal fin rays 1-2 in female. Origin of dorsal fin opposite second anal fin ray in male and first anal fin ray in female. Five pelvic fin rays. Twenty-three to 27 anal fin rays in male. Head length of male about 30% SL. Length of longest dorsal fin ray of male about 30% length of dorsal fin base. Body depth of male about 40% SL. Urogenital papilla of male connected to anal fin. Frontal squamation composed of four or five regularly distributed scales. About 20 neuromasts on supraorbital series.

Male reaching about 40 mm SL.

Coloration.- Male: sides of body light gray with about 20 dark bars. Unpaired fins greenish gray. Lower margin of pectoral fin and distal margin of anal fin with black contour. *Female*: sides of body pale brown with dark blotches. Unpaired fins hyaline with dark spots on dorsal and anal fins.

Distribution.- Arroyo Tres Cruces flood plains, Tacuarembó, central Uruguay.

Cynolebias adloffi Ahl
(Fig. 88)

Cynolebias adloffi Ahl, 1922:4 (original description; Porto Alegre, Rio Grande do Sul, Brazil).
Cynolebias atloffi; Ihering, 1931:257 (misspelling).

Diagnosis.- Frontal squamation composed of four or five regularly distributed scales; about 20

Fig. 88. *Cynolebias adloffi*, aquarium fish. Photo by A. Norman.

neuromasts in supraorbital series; male reaching about 40 mm SL; head length of male about 30% SL; length of longest dorsal fin ray of male about 40% length of dorsal fin base; five pelvic fin rays; no filamentous rays in dorsal fin of male; anal fin origin in front of dorsal fin origin; body depth of male about 40% SL; 23-27 anal fin rays in male; pectoral fin reaches to base of anal fin rays 6-7 in male; sides of body of male with about 10 bars; male with black spots on basal region of caudal fin and black margins on lower region of pectoral fin.

Description.- Dorsal and anal fins somewhat pointed in male, rounded in female. Caudal fin rounded. No filamentous rays in dorsal fin of male. Pectoral fin rounded. Posterior margin of pectoral fin reaches to base of anal fin rays 6-7 in male and to anus in female. Pelvic fin reaches to base of anal fin rays 2-3 in male and to anal fin rays 1-2 in female. Origin of dorsal fin opposite second anal fin ray in male and first anal fin ray in female. Five pelvic fin rays. Twenty-three to 27 anal fin rays in male. Head length of male about 30% SL. Length of longest dorsal fin ray of male about 40% length of dorsal fin base. Body depth of male about 40% SL. Frontal squamation composed of four or five regularly distributed scales. About

20 neuromasts in supraorbital series. Male reaching about 40 mm SL.

Coloration.- Male: sides of body light greenish gray with about ten dark bars. About three black spots on basal region of caudal fin. Unpaired fins greenish gray. *Female*: sides of body pale brown with dark blotches. About three black spots on basal region of caudal fin. Unpaired fins hyaline with dark spots.

Distribution.- Lowlands between São Leopoldo, Rio Grande do Sul, southern Brazil, and Chuy, Rocha, eastern Uruguay.

Cynolebias cheradophilus
Vaz-Ferreira, Soriano & Paulete
(Fig. 89-90)

Cynolebias cheradophilus Vaz-Ferreira, Soriano & Paulete, 1964:14 (original description; temporary swamps near Arroyo Valizas, Rocha, Uruguay).

Diagnosis.- Frontal squamation composed of about 20 irregularly distributed scales; about 30 neuromasts on supraorbital series; male reaching about 80 mm SL; dorsal and anal fins of male somewhat rounded; 20-22 anal fin rays in male; body sides of male with conspicuous dark bars.

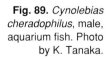

Fig. 89. *Cynolebias cheradophilus*, male, aquarium fish. Photo by K. Tanaka.

Fig. 90. *Cynolebias cheradophilus*, female, aquarium fish.

Description.- Dorsal and anal fins somewhat rounded in male, rounded in female. Caudal fin somewhat truncate. Pectoral fin rounded. Posterior margin of pectoral fin reaches to base of anal fin rays 1-2 in male and to base of pelvic fin in female. Pelvic fin reaches to base of anal fin rays 3-4 in male and to anal fin rays 1-2 in female. Origin of dorsal fin opposite anal fin rays 2-4. Six pelvic fin rays. Twenty to 22 anal fin rays in male. Frontal squamation about 20 irregularly distributed scales. About 30 neuromasts in supraorbital series. Male reaching about 80 mm SL.

Coloration.- *Male*: sides of body green with dark greenish gray bars. Unpaired fins dark greenish gray with light gray dots over dorsal fin. *Female*: sides of body pale brown with dark spots and bars. Unpaired fins hyaline.

Distribution.- Coastal plains of Rocha, eastern Uruguay.

Cynolebias prognathus Amato

Cynolebias prognathus Amato, 1986:7 (original description; Maravillas flood plains, La Coronolla, Rocha, Uruguay).

Diagnosis.- Frontal squamation composed of about 20 irregularly distributed scales; about 30 neuromasts on supraorbital series; male reaching about 80 mm SL; dorsal and anal fins of male somewhat rounded; 23-25 anal fin rays in male; body sides of male brown with bright yellowish brown blotches; lower jaw elongated.

Description.- Dorsal and anal fins somewhat rounded in male. Caudal fin rounded. Pectoral fin rounded. Posterior margin of pectoral fin reaches to base of fifth anal fin ray. Pelvic fin reaches to base of fifth anal fin ray. Origin of dorsal fin opposite anal fin rays 5-6. Six pelvic fin rays. Twenty-three to 25 anal fin rays in male. Frontal squamation composed of about 20 irregularly distributed scales. About 30 neuromasts in supraorbital series. Male reaching about 80 mm SL.

Coloration.- *Male*: sides of body brown with yellowish brown blotches. Unpaired fins reddish with dark blotches and stripes.

Remarks.- Only males are known.

Distribution.- Coastal plains near La Coronilla, Rocha, northeastern Uruguay.

Cynolebias wolterstorffi Ahl
(Figs. 91-92)

Cynolebias wolterstorffi Ahl, 1924:358 (original description; Porto Alegre, Brazil).

Cynolebias schreitmuelleri Ahl, 1934:308 (original description; Rio de Janeiro, Brazil [not confirmed; probably Rio Grande do Sul, Brazil]).

Fig. 91 (above). *Cynolebias wolterstorffi*, aquarium fish. Photo by K. Tanaka.
Fig. 92 (below). *Cynolebias wolterstorffi*, aquarium fish. Photo by A. Norman.

Cynolebias haerteli Schreitmuller, 1937:11 (published as a synonym of *C. schreitmuelleri*).

Diagnosis.- Frontal squamation composed of about 20 irregularly distributed scales; about 30 neuromasts on supraorbital series; male reaching about 80 mm SL; dorsal and anal fins of male somewhat pointed; 23-26 anal fin rays in male; body sides and unpaired fins of male dark brown with bright gray dots over unpaired fins; body depth of male about 35% SL; male with 35-40 scales in longitudinal series.

Description.- Dorsal and anal fins somewhat pointed in male, rounded in female. Caudal fin rounded. Pectoral fin rounded. Posterior margin of pectoral fin reaches to base of third anal fin ray in male and to urogenital papilla in female. Pelvic fin reaches to base of second anal fin ray in male and to urogenital papilla in female. Origin of dorsal fin opposite anal fin rays 2-4. Six pelvic fin rays. Twenty-three to 25 anal fin rays in male. Body depth of male about 35% SL. Male with 35-40 scales in longitudinal series. Frontal squamation composed of about 20 irregularly distributed scales. About 30 neuromasts in supraorbital series. Male reaching about 80 mm SL.

Coloration.- Male: sides of body and unpaired fins dark bluish brown, bright gray dots on unpaired fins. *Female*: sides of body pale brown with dark blotches. Unpaired fins hyaline.

Distribution.- Coastal lowlands of Rio Grande do Sul, southern Brazil, and Rocha, northeastern Uruguay.

Cynolebias elongatus Steindachner
(Fig. 93)

Cynolebias elongatus Steindachner, 1881:98 (original description; La Plata, Argentina).
Cynolebias robustus Günther, 1883:140 (original description; near San Antonio, Argentina).
Cynolebias holmbergi Berg, 1897:296 (original description; Arroyo Vivoratá, Mar Chiquita, Buenos Aires, Argentina).
Cynolebias spinifer Ahl, 1934:310 (original description; La Plata, Buenos Aires, Argentina).

Diagnosis.- Frontal squamation composed of about 20 irregularly distributed scales; about 30 neuromasts on supraorbital series; male reaching about 120 mm SL; dorsal and anal fins of male somewhat rounded; 23-25 anal fin rays in male; body sides and unpaired fins of male dark bluish brown with bright gray

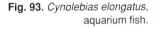

Fig. 93. *Cynolebias elongatus*, aquarium fish.

dots over unpaired fins; body depth of male about 30% SL; male with 45-75 scales in longitudinal series.

Description.- Dorsal and anal fins somewhat rounded in male, rounded in female. Caudal fin rounded. Pectoral fin rounded. Posterior margin of pectoral fin reaches to base of sixth anal fin ray in male and to second anal fin ray in female. Pelvic fin reaches to base of fourth anal fin ray in male and to second anal fin ray in female. Origin of dorsal fin opposite anal fin rays 2-4. Six pelvic fin rays. Twenty-three to 25 anal fin rays in male. Body depth of male about 30% SL. Male with 45-75 scales in longitudinal series. Frontal squamation composed of about 20 irregularly distributed scales. About 30 neuromasts in supraorbital series. Male reaching about 120 mm SL.

Coloration.- *Male*: sides of body and unpaired fins dark bluish brown; bright gray dots on unpaired fins. *Female*: sides of body pale brown with dark blotches. Unpaired fins hyaline.

Distribution.- Paraná and lower Paraguay flood plains, Salta, Corrientes, Entre Rios, and Buenos Aires, northern and northeastern Argentina.

Cynolebias griseus
Costa, Lacerda & Brasil
(Figs. 94-96)

Cynolebias griseus Costa, Lacerda & Brasil, 1990:11 (original description; temporary lagoon, Nova Roma, Goiás, Brazil).

Diagnosis.- Frontal squamation composed of about 20 irregularly distributed scales; about 25 neuromasts in supraorbital series; male reaching about 80 mm SL; dorsal and anal fins pointed in male; dark blotches present on posterodorsal region of head sides; origin of dorsal fin in front of anal fin origin; without filamentous rays in anal fin of male.

Description.- Dorsal and anal fins

Fig. 94. *Cynolebias griseus*, wild male from type locality, about 50 mm SL, not preserved. Photo by G. Brasil.

Fig. 95 (above). *Cynolebias griseus*, wild female from type locality, about 35 mm SL, not preserved. Photo by G. Brasil.
Fig. 96 (below). *Cynolebias griseus*, wild male from type locality, about 60 mm SL, not preserved. Photo by the author.

pointed in male, rounded in female. Caudal fin rounded. Pectoral fin rounded. Posterior margin of pectoral fin reaches to base of sixth anal fin ray in male and to anal fin rays 2-5 in female. Pelvic fin reaches to base of fourth anal fin ray in male and to anal fin rays 1-3 in female. Origin of anal fin opposite dorsal fin rays 1-3. Six pelvic fin rays. Frontal squamation composed of about 20 irregularly distributed scales. About 30 neuromasts in supraorbital series. Male reaching about 80 mm SL.

Coloration.- Male: sides of body bright bluish gray. Dark blotches on posterodorsal region of head sides. Unpaired fins dark gray with bright gray dots over dorsal fin and upper region of caudal fin. *Female*: sides of body pale brown with dark dots and blotches. Unpaired fins hyaline.

Distribution.- Rio Paraná basin, Goiás, central Brazil.

Cynolebias microphthalmus Costa & Brasil, new species
(Fig. 97)

Holotype.- MZUSP 42312, male, 97.5 mm SL; Brazil: Rio Grande do norte: Mossoró; G.C. Brasil, IX 1972.

Paratypes.- MZUSP 38343, 3 males, 89.9, 96.8 and 97.9 mm SL; collected with the holotype.

Diagnosis.- Frontal squamation composed of about 20 irregularly distributed scales; about 30 neuromasts in supraorbital series; male reaching about 100 mm SL; dorsal and anal fins pointed in male; dark blotches on posterodorsal region of head sides; origin of dorsal fin behind anal fin origin; anal fin of male with filamentous rays; eye diameter of adult male 15.4-17.2 % SL; unpaired fins of male dark brown.

Description (male).- Dorsal and anal fins pointed. Caudal fin rounded. Pectoral fin rounded. Posterior margin of pectoral fin reaches to base of fifth anal fin ray. Pelvic fin reaches to base of anal fin rays 1-3. Origin of dorsal fin opposite anal fin rays 6-7. Six pelvic fin rays. Frontal squamation composed of about 20 irregularly distributed scales. Neuromasts 30 in supraorbital, 30 in infraorbital, and 28 in preopercular series. Meristic and morphometric data are given in Table 2.

Coloration.- Sides of body brownish gray. Unpaired and pelvic fins dark brown. Dark blotches on posterodorsal region of head sides. Pectoral fin hyaline.

Remarks.- No females were preserved for study. It is possible that the material collected by Antenor de Carvalho near Russas, Ceará, Brazil,

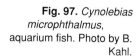

Fig. 97. *Cynolebias microphthalmus*, aquarium fish. Photo by B. Kahl.

and designated by Myers (1952) as *Cynolebias regani* (*nomem nudum*) belongs to the new species, judging from the proximity of the localities. No specimen from Ceará was available for the present revision, except a female (50.2 mm SL, MNRJ 11275), prohibiting adequate comparisons.

Etymology.- From the Greek (small) and (eye), in reference to the small eye of the male of this species; treated as a noun in apposition.

Cynolebias perforatus Costa & Brasil
(Fig. 98)

Cynolebias perforatus Costa & Brasil, 1991:56 (original description; temporary pool near Januária, Minas Gerais, Brazil).

Diagnosis.- Frontal squamation composed of about 20 irregularly distributed scales; male with 35-39 neuromasts in supraorbital, 27-30 in infraorbital, and 37-38 in preopercular series; male reaching about 90 mm SL; dorsal fin pointed in male; dark blotches on posterodorsal region of head sides; origin of dorsal fin behind anal fin origin; anal fin of male with filamentous rays; eye diameter of adult male 19.7-20.5% SL; male with pale gray dots on unpaired fins; distance between supraorbital series of neuromasts 12.0-15.0% HL in male.

Description.- Dorsal and anal fins pointed in male, rounded in female.

Caudal fin rounded. Pectoral fin rounded. Posterior margin of pectoral fin reaches to base of fifth anal fin ray in male, to urogenital papilla in female. Pelvic fin reaches to base of third anal fin ray in male and to second anal fin ray in female. Origin of dorsal fin opposite anal fin rays 5-6 in male, anal fin rays 3-4 in female. Six pelvic fin rays. Eye diameter of adult male 19.7-20.5% SL. Distance between supraorbital series of neuromasts 12.0-15.0% HL in male. Frontal squamation composed of about 20 irregularly distributed scales. Neuromasts in male 35-39 in supraorbital, 35-36 in infraorbital, and 37-38 in preopercular series. Male reaching about 90 mm SL.

Coloration.- *Male*: sides of body brown. Unpaired fins dark brown with pale grays dots. Dark blotches on posterodorsal region of head sides. *Female*: sides of body pale brown with dark bars and spots. Unpaired fins hyaline with faint gray spots on dorsal and anal fins.

Distribution.- Middle São Francisco flood plains, Minas Gerais, central Brazil.

Cynolebias albipunctatus Costa & Brasil
(Fig. 99)

Cynolebias albipunctatus Costa & Brasil, 1991:58 (original description; temporary pool near Uauá, Juazeiro, Bahia, Brazil).

Fig. 98.
Cynolebias perforatus, holotype, male, 90.7 mm SL, MZUSP 41376.

Fig. 99. *Cynolebias albipunctatus*, wild male from type locality, about 95 mm SL, not preserved. Photo by G. Brasil.

Diagnosis.- Frontal squamation composed of about 20 irregularly distributed scales; male with 25-30 neuromasts in supraorbital, 25-31 in infraorbital, and 25-31 in preopercular series; male reaching about 100 mm SL; dorsal fin pointed in male; dark blotches on posterodorsal region of head sides; origin of dorsal fin behind anal fin origin; anal fin of male with filamentous rays; eye diameter of adult male 19.4-20.8% SL; male with bright white dots on body sides and unpaired fins; distance between supraorbital series of neuromasts 21.0-23.0% HL in male; length of anal fin base of adult male 35.0-37.0 % SL.

Description.- Dorsal and anal fins pointed in male, rounded in female. Caudal fin rounded. Pectoral fin rounded. Posterior margin of pectoral fin reaches to base of anal fin rays 1-4 in male, to base of pelvic fin in female. Pelvic fin reaches to base of anal fin rays 2-3 in male, to urogenital papilla in female. Origin of dorsal fin opposite anal fin rays 4-7 in male, anal fin rays 2-4 in female. Six pelvic fin rays. Eye diameter of adult male 19.4-20.8% SL. Distance between supraorbital series of neuromasts 21.0-23.0% HL in male. Length of anal fin base of adult male 35.0-37.0% SL. Frontal squamation composed of about 20 irregularly distributed scales. Neuromasts in male 25-30 in supraorbital, 27-30 in infraorbital, and 25-31 in preopercular series. Male reaching about 100 mm SL.

Coloration.- Male: sides of body and unpaired fins dark brown with bright white dots. Dark blotches on posterodorsal region of head sides. *Female*: sides of body pale brown with dark bars and spots. Unpaired fins hyaline with dark spots.

Distribution.- Middle São Francisco flood plains, Bahia, northeastern Brazil.

Cynolebias porosus Steindachner
(Fig. 100)

Cynolebias porosus Steindachner, 1876:125 (original description; Pernambuco, Brazil).

Diagnosis.- Frontal squamation composed of about 20 irregularly distributed scales; male with 24-26 neuromasts in supraorbital, 28-29 in infraorbital, and 25-29 in preopercular series; male reaching about 80 mm SL; dorsal fin pointed in male; dark blotches on posterodorsal region of head sides; origin of dorsal fin behind anal fin origin; anal fin of male with filamentous rays; eye diameter of adult male 22.0-23.0% SL; male with pale gray dots on body sides and unpaired fins; distance between supraorbital series of neuromasts 19.5-21.5% HL in male; length of anal fin base of adult male 31.5-32.5% SL.

Description.- Dorsal and anal fins pointed in male, rounded in female. Caudal fin rounded. Pectoral fin rounded. Posterior margin of pectoral fin reaches to base of anal fin rays 2-4 in male, to urogenital papilla in female. Pelvic fin reaches to base of anal fin rays 2-3. Origin of dorsal fin opposite anal fin rays 4-6 in male, anal fin rays 3-4 in female. Six pelvic fin rays. Eye diameter of adult male 22.0-23.0% SL. Distance between supraorbital series of neuromasts 19.5-21.5% HL in male. Length of anal fin base of adult male 31.5-32.5% SL. Frontal squamation composed of about 20 irregularly distributed scales. Neuromasts in male 24-26 in supraorbital, 28-29 in infraorbital, and 25-29 in preopercular series. Male reaching about 80 mm SL.

Coloration.- Male: sides of body brown with faint bars and pale gray

Fig. 100. *Cynolebias porosus*, wild male from Capim Grosso, about 50 mm SL, not preserved. Photo by G. Brasil.

dots. Unpaired fins dark gray with pale gray dots. Dark blotches on posterodorsal region of head sides. *Female*: sides of body pale brown with dark blotches. Unpaired fins hyaline.

Distribution.- Middle São Francisco, Vaza Barris, and Itapicuru basins, Pernambuco, and Bahia, northeastern Brazil.

LEPTOLEBIAS Myers

Leptolebias Myers, 1952:140 (type species *Cynopoecilus marmoratus* Ladiges, 1934, by original designation; (proposed as subgenus)).

Diagnosis.- Posterodorsal surface of urohyal sinuous; female with homogeneous pale brown coloration on body sides, without dark markings.

Description.- Anterior portion of anal fin of male not modified. Anal and dorsal fins moderate in length. Length of anal fin base of male 19.5-28.5% SL. Caudal fin of male somewhat truncate to lanceolate, length about 30% SL; about 30% of caudal scaled along longitudinal axis. Pectoral fin rounded, length about 25% SL. Pelvic fins with united bases and five or six rays. Male and female with same number of dorsal fin rays. Urogenital papilla moderate. Branchiostegal membrane moderate. Male reaching about 30 mm SL.

Dorsal surface of head with scales neither reduced nor arranged in circular pattern. Mesial borders of anterocentral scales not overlapping. Anterior and posterior portions of supraorbital series of neuromasts united; anterior portion with four to six neuromasts; posterior portion with four to six aligned neuromasts. Neuromast on dermosphenotic reduced. Preopercular canal absent.

Dentary moderate; dorsal and ventral surfaces not parallel. Ascending process of premaxilla narrow and without concavity in base. Vomer without teeth. Anguloarticular with anteromedian process moderate and anteroventral process reduced. Upper tip of quadrate without anterior expansion, posterior horizontal process moderate. Symplectic elongated. Mesopterygoid reduced. Upper tip of preopercle sharp and moderate.

Dermosphenotic absent. Lacrimal moderate, widened in upper portion and little twisted. Supraoccipital process horizontally oriented. Urohyal deep, with sinuous posterodorsal tip. First epibranchial larger than second and third. Interarcual cartilage about 60% of length of second epibranchial. No molariform teeth in branchial apparatus. Basihyal short and somewhat broad. Proximal edge of first hypobranchial not bifid.

Ten to 13 precaudal and 14 to 17 caudal vertebrae. First precaudal and caudal vertebrae without neural prezygapophysis. Proximal radials of anal fin widened; second, third, and fourth not smaller than posterior proximal radials. Pectoral radials scale-like. Supracleithrum elongated. Lower tip of cleithrum without anterior expansion. Posttemporal without lower process.

Male and female with distinct color patterns. Body sides of males with stripes or bars or spots. Females with homogeneous light brown coloration on sides of body; without dark markings.

Male during courtship with unpaired fins erected and twisted. Fertilization external. Egg with reticulate surface and mushroom-like prolongations. Egg diameter 0.8 to 1.0 mm. Development annual.

Seven species are included.- *L. minimus, L. cruzi, L. fluminensis, L. leitaoi, L. marmoratus, L. sandrii,* and *L. aureoguttatus.*

Distribution.- Coastal lowlands

between southern Bahia State and Paraná State, eastern Brazil (Fig. 101).

Generic Intrarelationships.- Numbers in parenthesis refer to apomorphic states of the cladogram of Figure 102.

Leptolebias minimus and *L. cruzi* share two synapomorphies:

    (1) - Caudal fin with bars in male. No Cynolebiatinae species has this condition, except for *Cynolebias myersi, C. magnificus, C. flammeus,* and *Plesiolebias aruana.* It is considered homoplasic for these species.

    (2) - Maxilla wide. The maxilla of *L. minimus* and *L. cruzi* is wider than that of any species of Cynolebiatinae (Fig. 103).

Leptolebias fluminensis, L. leitaoi, L. marmoratus, L. sandrii, and *L. aureoguttatus* share two synapomorphies:

    (3) - Caudal fin elliptical to lanceolate in male. In other species of *Leptolebias* and related genera, the caudal fin of the male is rounded to truncate, except in *Cynolebias myersi, C. bokermanni,* and *C. constanciae,*

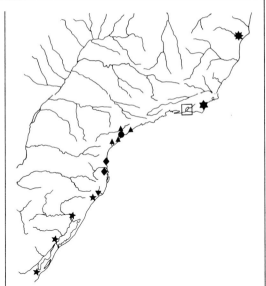

Fig. 101. Geographic distribution of *Leptolebias, Campellolebias,* and *Cynopoecilus* (some symbols represent more than one collecting locality). Eight tip star: *L. leitaoi;* six tip star: *L. cruzi;* square: *L. minimus, L. marmoratus, L. sandri* and *L. fluminensis;* triangle: *L. aureoguttatus;* circle: *Camp. dorsimaculatus;* lozenge: *Camp. chrysolineatus;* inverted triangle: *Camp. brucei;* five tip star: *Cynop. melanotaenia.*

where the similar state is considered an independent acquisition.

    (4) - Second pharyngobranchial teeth absent. All other species of

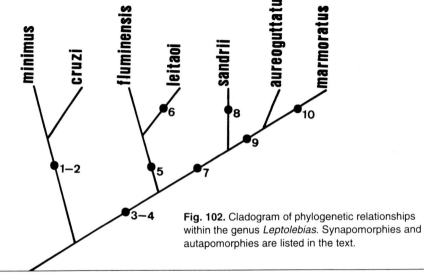

Fig. 102. Cladogram of phylogenetic relationships within the genus *Leptolebias.* Synapomorphies and autapomorphies are listed in the text.

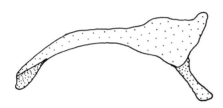

Fig. 103. Left maxilla of *Leptolebias cruzi.*

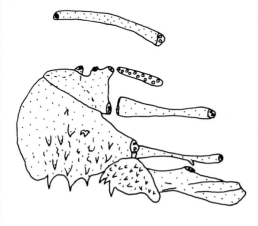

Fig. 104. Left dorsal gill arch of *Leptolebias aureoguttatus*, ventral view.

Fig. 105. Fifth ceratobranchial of *Leptolebias leitaoi*, dorsal view (teeth not represented).

Cynolebiatinae have teeth on second pharyngobranchial, except *Cynolebias porosus* and closely related species. This apomorphic state is considered to be independently acquired in the two groups (Fig. 104).

Leptolebias fluminensis and *L. leitaoi* share one synapomorphy:

(5) - Fifth ceratobranchial narrow. In these two species the fifth ceratobranchial is narrower than in any other species of Cynolebiatinae (Fig. 105).

Leptolebias leitaoi has a very evident autapomorphy:

(6) - Hooks in inner surface of pectoral fin of male. No other species of Rivulidae has hooks in the pectoral fin.

Leptolebias sandrii, L. marmoratus, and *L. aureoguttatus* share one synapomorphy:

(7) - Opercular region of male with a horizontal red stripe. No other species of Cynolebiatinae has this color pattern.

Leptolebias sandrii has a very evident autapomorphy:

(8) - Sides of body of male with zig-zag bars. No other species of Rivulidae has this color pattern.

Leptolebias marmoratus and *L. aureoguttatus* share one synapomorphy:

(9) - Yellow longitudinal stripes on caudal fin of male. No other species of Cynolebiatinae has these stripes.

Leptolebias marmoratus has a very evident autapomorphy:

(10) - Caudal fin of male asymmetrical. No other species of Cynolebiatinae has an

asymmetrical shape to the caudal fin.

Key to the species of *Leptolebias*

1. - Caudal fin of male somewhat truncate, with dark bars 2
   - Caudal fin of male elliptical or lanceolate, without dark bars ... 3
2. - Sixteen to 20 anal fin rays (modal number 18); length of anal fin base 25.7-34.5% SL ($\overline{X}$ = 29.7) in male, and 20.5-25.8% SL ($\overline{X}$ = 23.1) in female; male with very conspicuous dark bars on unpaired fins .... *L. minimus*
   - Fourteen to 17 anal fin rays (modal number 15); length of anal fin base 22.3-27.5% SL ($\overline{X}$ = 24.6) in male, and 17.9- 21.4% SL ($\overline{X}$ = 19.3) in female; male with faint bars on base of unpaired fins .... *L. cruzi*
3. - Twenty-one to 24 caudal fin rays; male without longitudinal stripes on opercular region 4
   - Twenty-six to 29 caudal fin rays; male with longitudinal stripe on opercular region 5
4. - Dorsal fin origin opposite 7th or 8th anal fin ray in male; body

sides of male without bars; pectoral fin of male without hooks .... *L. fluminensis*
   - Dorsal fin origin opposite third anal fin ray in male; body sides of male with dark bars; pectoral fin of male with hooks in inner surface .... *L. leitaoi*
5. - Caudal fin of male with asymmetrical shape; male with yellow stripes on body sides .... *L. marmoratus*
   - Caudal fin of male with symmetrical shape; male without yellow stripes on body sides 6
6. - Dorsal fin origin opposite anal fin rays 6-7 in male; body sides of male with zig-zag blue bars .... *L. sandrii*
   - Dorsal fin origin opposite anal fin rays 3-5 in male; body sides of male without bars .... *L. aureoguttatus*

***Leptolebias minimus* (Myers)**
(Figs. 106-109)

Cynolebias minimus Myers, 1942:109 (original description; cane-brake one mile East of Itaquahy (Itaguai), Rio de Janeiro, Brazil).

Fig. 106. *Leptolebias minimus,* wild male from type locality, about 25 mm SL, not preserved. Photo by the author.

Cynolebias (Cynopoecilus)
  splendens (non *Cynolebias*
  splendens Myers, 1942);
  Ladiges,1955:230; Schroeter,
  1956:63 (misidentifications).
Cynopoecilus splendens (non
  Cynolebias splendens Myers,
  1942); Siegel, 1958:200
  (misidentification).
Cynolebias ladigesi Foersch,
  1958:257 (original description,
  pools 80 km NW from Rio de
  Janeiro).
Cynopoecilus minimus; Seegers,
  1980:134.
Cynolebias opalescens (non
  Cynolebias opalescens Myers, 1942);
  Huber, 1981:11 (erroneous
  synonymy).
Cynolebias fractifasciatus Costa,
  1988a:562 (original description;
  swamp near Inoã, Maricá, Rio de
  Janeiro, Brazil) new synonymy
Leptolebias fractifasciatus; Costa,
  1990a:68.
Leptolebias minimus; Costa, 1990a:68.

  Diagnosis.- Caudal fin of male
somewhat truncate and with very
conspicuous dark bars; 16-20 anal fin
rays (modal number 18).
  Description.- Dorsal and anal fins
pointed in male, rounded in female.
Posterior margin of pectoral fin
reaches to urogenital papilla in male
and to base of pelvic fin in female.
Pelvic fin
reaches to anal
fin rays 1-3 in
male and to
urogenital
papilla in
female. Origin
of dorsal fin
opposite anal
fin rays 4-5 in
male and anal
fin rays 2-4 in
female. Sixteen
to 20 anal fin

Fig. 107. *Leptolebias minimus*, wild male from Inoã, type locality of *L. fractifasciatus*, about 20 mm SL, not preserved. Photo by the author.

rays (modal number 18).
  Coloration.- Male: body sides blue or
green with crimson scale edges.
Unpaired fins blue or green with
conspicuous transverse crimson bars.
Female: as described for the genus.
  Distribution.- Coastal plains around
Baía de Guanabara, Rio de Janeiro,
northeastern Brazil.
  Remarks.- In the original
description of *C. fractifasciatus*, Costa
(1988a) distinguished it from *C.
minimus* by the male having broken
and bifid bars on the caudal fin and
bars on the body sides. However,
after examining additional specimens
with intermediate patterns, which

Fig. 108. *Leptolebias minimus*, aquarium fish. Photo by K. Tanaka.

Fig. 109. *Leptolebias minimus*, aquarium fish. Photo by E. Taylor.

Diagnosis.- Caudal fin of male somewhat truncate and with faint bars on basal region; 14-17 anal fin rays (modal number 15).

Description.- Dorsal and anal fins pointed in male, rounded in female. Posterior margin of pectoral fin reaches to base of pelvic fin. Pelvic fin reaches to first anal fin ray in male and to urogenital papilla in female. Origin of dorsal fin opposite anal fin rays 4-6 in male and anal fin rays 3-5 in female. Fourteen to 17 anal fin rays (modal number 15).

Coloration.- Male: body sides dark green with reddish brown scale contours. Unpaired fins reddish brown with faint transverse bars on basal region. *Female:* as described for the genus.

were found in new localities, *L. fractifasciatus* is now considered a subjective synonym of *L. minimus*.

Leptolebias cruzi (Costa)
(Fig. 110)

Cynolebias cruzi Costa, 1988a:563 (original description; swamp near Barra de São João, Rio de Janeiro, Brazil).
Leptolebias cruzi; Costa, 1990a:68.

Fig. 110. *Leptolebias cruzi*, wild male from type locality, about 20 mm SL, not preserved. Photo by G. Brasil.

Fig. 111. *Leptolebias fluminensis*, wild male from Maricá, about 25 mm SL, not preserved. Photo by G. Brasil.

Distribution.- Coastal plains near Rio São João, Rio de Janeiro, southeastern Brazil.

Remarks.- The only known biotope of the species is in an advanced state of decomposition. *Leptolebias cruzi* must be considered a species threatened with extinction.

Leptolebias fluminensis (Faria & Muller)
(Fig. 111)

Cynopoecilus fluminensis Faria & Muller, 1937:99 (original description; Rio de Janeiro, Brazil).

Cynolebias opalescens Myers, 1942:107 (original description; ponds along base of the Serra de Petrópolis, Rio de Janeiro, Brazil).

Cynolebias nanus Cruz & Peixoto, 1984:90 (original description; between Cava and Tinguá, Nova Iguaçú, Rio de Janeiro) new synonymy

Cynolebias citrinipinnis Costa, Lacerda & Tanizaki, 1988b:22 (original description; pool in Maricá, Rio de Janeiro, Brazil) new synonymy

Leptolebias citrinipinnis; Costa, 1990a:68.

Leptolebias fluminensis; Costa, 1990a:68.

Leptolebias nanus; Costa, 1990a:68.

Diagnosis.- Caudal fin of male lanceolate; dorsal fin origin opposite anal fin rays 7-8 in male; pectoral fin without hooks; no longitudinal stripes on opercular region of male.

Description.- Dorsal and anal fins pointed in male, rounded in female. Posterior margin of pectoral fin reaches to anus in male and to base of pelvic fin in female. Pelvic fin reaches to anal fin rays 1-3 in male and to urogenital papilla in female. Origin of dorsal fin opposite anal fin rays 7-8 in male and anal fin rays 6-7 in female. No hooks on pectoral fin.

Coloration.- *Male*: body sides green or blue with pink scale edges. Unpaired fins yellowish green to blue with dark reddish brown spots and striae. Vertical dark crimson markings on opercular region. *Female*: as described for the genus.

Distribution.- Coastal plains around Baía de Guanabara, Rio de Janeiro, southeastern Brazil.

Remarks.- Most of the rare

mentions of this species referred to *Cynolebias opalescens*. Myers did not recognize the validity of the descriptions by Faria & Muller (1937) because they appeared in a journal with little circulation (Costa & Lacerda, 1988b). However, the *Cynopoecilus fluminensis* description fully satisfies the conditions of the International Code of Zoological Nomenclature (Costa & Lacerda, 1988b).

Due to the rareness of samples of *L. fluminensis* topotypes and its disappearance in the type locality, two synonyms were subsequently described— *Cynolebias nanus* Cruz & Peixoto and *C. citrinipinnis* Costa, Lacerda & Tanizaki. A study of additional specimens collected in the type locality of *L. citrinipinnis* during the last years provided data about character variability, making it possible to synonymize all these species.

Leptolebias fluminensis has appeared in lists of threatened species. After exhaustive field work in the distribution area of the species, it has been recorded only in four localities: Serra de Petrópolis, Vila de Cava, Seropédica, and Barra de Maricá. In Serra de Petrópolis the species has not been found since 1944, and in Vila de Cava, not since 1981. In Seropédica, a single specimen was collected in 1984. In Barra de Maricá *L. fluminensis* is easily found but the swamp is being destroyed. Therefore, *L. fluminensis* may be indicated as being strongly threatened with extinction.

Leptolebias leitaoi (Cruz & Peixoto) new combination
(Fig. 112)

Cynolebias leitaoi Cruz & Peixoto, 1992:638 (original description; swamp near Rio Mucuri, Southern Bahia, Brazil).

Diagnosis.- Caudal fin lanceolate in male; dorsal fin origin opposite third anal fin ray in male; pectoral fin of male with hooks in inner surface; no longitudinal stripes on opercular region.

Description.- Dorsal and anal fins pointed in male, rounded in female. Posterior margin of pectoral fin reaches to base of pelvic fin. Pelvic fin reaches to first anal fin ray in male and to urogenital papilla in female. Origin of dorsal fin opposite third anal fin ray. Pectoral fin of male with hooks in inner surface.

Coloration.- Male: body sides green or blue with crimson scale edges and crimson bars. Unpaired fins reddish with green spots. *Female*: as described for the genus.

Distribution.- Coastal plains in Rio Mucuri basin, Bahia, eastern Brazil.

Leptolebias marmoratus (Ladiges)

Cynopoecilus marmoratus Ladiges, 1934:73 (original description; Rio de Janeiro, Brazil).

Cynopoecilus sicheleri Ribeiro, 1939:363 (original description; base of the Serra de Petrópolis, Rio de Janeiro, Brazil).

Cynolebias zingiberinus Myers, 1942:108 (original description; base of Serra de Petrópolis, Rio de Janeiro, Brazil).

Cynolebias marmoratus; Myers, 1944:204.

Leptolebias marmoratus; Costa, 1990a:68.

Diagnosis.- Caudal fin of male asymmetrically lanceolate; longitudinal stripe on opercular region of male; male with yellow stripes on body sides.

Description.- Dorsal and anal fins pointed in male, rounded in female. Posterior margin of pectoral fin reaches to anus in male and to base of pelvic fin in female. Pelvic fin reaches to anal fin rays

Fig. 112. *Leptolebias leitaoi*, aquarium material, not preserved. Photo by M. Notare.

1-3 in male and to urogenital papilla in female. Origin of dorsal fin opposite anal fin rays 2-4. No hooks on pectoral fin.

Coloration.- Male: body sides reddish brown with two interrupted longitudinal stripes on and below midline. Unpaired fins yellowish with red spots. *Female*: as described for the genus.

Distribution.- Coastal plains near Baía de Guanabara, Rio de Janeiro, southeastern Brazil.

Remarks.- There are rare mentions to this species in the scientific literature. It has not been found since 1944 and unsuccessful investigations in recent field work suggest that it is extinct.

Leptolebias sandrii (Faria & Muller)
(Fig. 113)

Gynopoecilus sandrii Faria & Muller, 1937:98 (original description; Rio de Janeiro, Brazil [misprint of

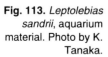

Fig. 113. *Leptolebias sandrii*, aquarium material. Photo by K. Tanaka.

Cynopoecilus]).
Cynolebias splendens Myers, 1942:110 (original description; ponds along base of Serra de Petrópolis, Brazil).
Cynolebias opalescens (non *Cynolebias opalescens* Myers, 1942); Huber, 1981:11 (erroneous synonymy).
Cynolebias sandrii; Lacerda, 1987:34.
Leptolebias sandrii; Costa, 1990a:68.

Diagnosis.- Caudal fin of male symmetrical, elliptical to somewhat lanceolate; longitudinal stripe in opercular region of male; dorsal fin origin opposite anal fin rays 6-7; male with zig-zag blue bars on body sides.

Description.- Dorsal and anal fins pointed in male, rounded in female. Posterior margin of pectoral fin reaches to urogenital papilla in male and to base of pelvic fin in female. Pelvic fin reaches to anal fin rays 1-3 in male and to urogenital papilla in female. Origin of dorsal fin opposite anal fin rays 6-7.

Coloration.- *Male*: body sides red with zig-zag blue bars. Opercular region golden with red longitudinal stripe and red spots. Unpaired fins red with blue striae. Dorsal fin with large golden stripe on distal edge. *Female*: as described for the genus.

Distribution.- Coastal plains near Baía de Guanabara, Rio de Janeiro, Brazil.

Remarks.- Like *L. fluminensis*, *L. sandrii* has been cited as *Cynolebias splendens* because the original publication of *Cynopoecilus sandrii* occurred in a Brazilian journal of little circulation (Costa & Lacerda, 1988b). Myers did not recognize the validity of the Faria & Muller paper and described *C. splendens* as new species (Myers, 1942).

Leptolebias sandrii figures in the list of species threatened with extinction. It has not been collected between 1944 and 1985. Presently, this species is found only in a single swamp close to the type locality. Thus it must be considered a very endangered species.

Leptolebias aureoguttatus (Cruz)
(Figs. 114-116)

Cynolebias aureoguttatus Myers, 1952:131 (nom. nudum).
Cynolebias paranaguensis Myers, 1952:131 (nom. nudum).
Cynolebias aureoguttatus Cruz, 1974:20 (original description; Paranaguá-Matinhos road, Paraná, Brazil).
Leptolebias aureoguttatus; Costa, 1990a:68.

Diagnosis.- Caudal fin of male symmetrical and elliptical; longitudinal stripe on opercular region of male;

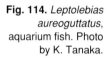

Fig. 114. *Leptolebias aureoguttatus*, aquarium fish. Photo by K. Tanaka.

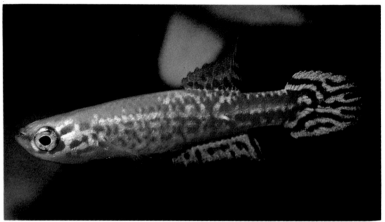

Fig. 115 (above). *Leptolebias aureoguttatus*, wild male from type locality, about 25 mm SL, not preserved. Photo by the author.
Fig. 116 (below). *Leptolebias aureoguttatus*, wild male from Itanhaém, about 25 mm SL, not preserved. Photo by G. Brasil.

dorsal fin origin opposite anal fin rays 3-5; male without bars on body sides.

Description.- Dorsal and anal fins pointed in male, rounded in female. Posterior margin of pectoral fin reaches to urogenital papilla in male and to base of pelvic fin in female. Pelvic fin reaches to first anal fin ray in male and to urogenital papilla in female. Origin of dorsal fin opposite anal fin rays 3-5.

Coloration.- Male: body sides blue to golden with crimson scale edges. Opercular region blue to green with a crimson longitudinal stripe and crimson spots. Unpaired fins blue to golden with crimson spots and striae. Distinct golden stripe on upper edge of caudal fin and another on lower edge. *Female*: as described for the genus.

Distribution.- Coastal plains between Itanhaém, São Paulo, and Paranaguá, Paraná, southeastern Brazil.

Remarks.- The first reference to this species was made by Myers (1952) when he referred to both *Cynolebias aureoguttatus* and *C. paranaguensis* (referring to the same species) without descriptions, thus erecting two *nomina nuda*. Cruz (1974) formally described *C. aureoguttatus*, making it an available name.

CAMPELLOLEBIAS Vaz-Ferreira & Sierra

Campellolebias Vaz-Ferreira & Sierra, 1974:1 (type species *Campellolebias brucei* Vaz-Ferreira & Sierra, 1974, by original designation).

Diagnosis.- Anterior portion of anal fin of male isolated by notch in anal fin membrane; urogenital papilla of male elongated and connected to anterior portion of anal fin; ventral region of head of male with three longitudinal dark stripes; internal fertilization; chorion without prolongations.

Description.- Anterior portion of anal fin of male isolated by notch in anal fin membrane. Anal and dorsal fins moderate. Anal fin base of male 19.5-28.5% SL. Caudal fin of male somewhat truncate, length about 35% SL; about 35% of caudal scaled along longitudinal axis. Pectoral fin rounded, length about 20% SL. Pelvic fins with separated bases and six rays. Male and female with same number of dorsal fin rays. Urogenital papilla of male elongated and connected to anterior portion of anal fin. Branchiostegal membrane moderate. Male reaching about 40 mm SL.

Dorsal surface of head with scales neither reduced nor arranged in circular pattern. Mesial borders of anterocentral scales not overlapping. Anterior and posterior portions of supraorbital series of neuromasts united; anterior portion with six to eight neuromasts; posterior portion with four to seven aligned neuromasts. Neuromast on dermosphenotic reduced. Preopercular canal absent.

Dentary moderate; dorsal and ventral surfaces not parallel. Ascending process of premaxilla narrow and without basal concavity. Vomer without teeth. Anguloarticular with anteromedian process moderate and anteroventral process reduced. Upper tip of quadrate without anterior expansion and posterior horizontal process moderate. Symplectic elongated. Mesopterygoid reduced. Upper tip of preopercle sharp and moderate in length.

Dermosphenotic absent. Lacrimal moderate, widened in upper portion and little twisted. Supraoccipital process horizontally oriented. Urohyal moderate in depth, with rounded posterodorsal tip. First epibranchial larger than second and third. Interarcual cartilage about 60% length of second epibranchial. No molariform teeth in branchial apparatus. Basihyal short and somewhat broad. Proximal edge of first hypobranchial not bifid.

Thirteen precaudal and 16 caudal vertebrae. First precaudal and caudal vertebrae without neural prezygapophysis. Proximal radials of anal fin narrow; second, third, and fourth not smaller than posterior proximal radials. Pectoral radials scale-like. Supracleithrum elongated. Lower tip of cleithrum without anterior expansion. Posttemporal without lower process.

Male and female with distinct color patterns. Male with dark longitudinal stripes or bars on body sides. Female with dark blotches on body sides.

Males during courtship with unpaired fins erected and twisted. Fertilization internal. Egg with reticulate surface and without prolongations. Egg diameter about 1.2 mm. Development annual.

Three species are included: *C. brucei*, *C. chrysolineatus*, and *C. dorsimaculatus*.

Distribution.- Coastal lowlands

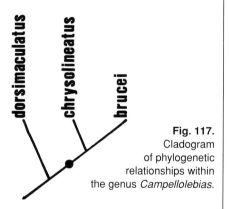

Fig. 117. Cladogram of phylogenetic relationships within the genus *Campellolebias*.

between southern São Paulo and southern Santa Catarina, Brazil (Fig. 101).

Remarks.- *Campellolebias* was recently revised by Costa et al. (1989).

Generic Intrarelationships.- The meristic, morphometric, and osteological similarities of *Campellolebias* species makes it difficult to elaborate a phylogenetic

hypothesis. Only the longitudinal rows of brilliant spots on the body sides of males support the cladogram of Figure 117. This color pattern, shared by *C. chrysolineatus* and *C. brucei*, is unique among fishes of the subfamily Cynolebiatinae.

Key to the species of *Campellolebias*

1. - Male with longitudinal rows of brilliant spots on body sides; no black spot in posterior region of dorsal fin; caudal fin reddish 2
   - Male with dark bars on body sides; large black spot in posterior region of dorsal fin; caudal fin greenish with dark spots .... *C. dorsimaculatus*
2. - Male with body sides purplish pink and golden spots composing longitudinal lines; 14 rays in posterior region of anal fin; males between 25.0 and 30.0 mm SL with body depth 24.5 to 27.0% SL .... *C. chrysolineatus*
   - Male with body sides crimson and longitudinal rows of green spots; 12 or 13 rays in posterior region of anal fin; males between 25.0 and 30.0 mm SL with body depth 28.5 to 30.0% SL .... *C. brucei*

Campellolebias dorsimaculatus Costa, Lacerda & Brasil
(Figs. 118-119)

Campellolebias dorsimaculatus Costa, Lacerda & Brasil, 1989:66 (original description; puddle in forest edge, Iguape, São Paulo, Brazil).

Diagnosis.- Male with dark bars on body sides; large black spot in posterior region of dorsal fin; caudal fin greenish with dark spots.

Description.- Dorsal and anal fins pointed in male, rounded in female. Posterior margin of pectoral fin reaches to modified anterior portion of

Fig. 118 (above). *Campellolebias dorsimaculatus*, wild male from type locality, about 25 mm SL, not preserved. Photo by G. Brasil.
Fig. 119 (below). *Campellolebias dorsimaculatus*, wild female from type locality, about 20 mm SL, not preserved. Photo by G. Brasil.

anal fin in male, about to middle of distance from pelvic fin base to anus in female. Pelvic fin reaches to anal fin rays 1-2 in male and to urogenital papilla in female. Origin of anal fin opposite dorsal fin rays 2-3 in male and dorsal fin rays 4-5 in female. Male with 12 or 13 rays in posterior region of anal fin.

Coloration.- Male: Body sides purplish brown with dark bars alternating with small golden spots. Dorsal fin pale reddish brown with dark spots in basal region and large black spot in posterior region. Caudal fin greenish with dark brown spots. *Female*: Body sides pale brown with dark brown blotches forming diffused bars. Unpaired fins hyaline with black spots.

Distribution.- Coastal lowlands near Iguape, São Paulo, southeastern Brazil.

Campellolebias chrysolineatus Costa, Lacerda & Brasil
(Fig. 120)

Campellolebias chrysolineatus Costa, Lacerda & Brasil, 1989:69 (original description; puddle in forest edge, Araquari, Santa Catarina, Brazil).

Diagnosis.- Male with body sides purplish pink, rectangular golden spots composing seven longitudinal lines; 14 rays in posterior region of anal fin.

Description.- Shape and position of fins as in *C. dorsimaculatus*. Males with 14 rays in posterior region of anal fin.

Coloration.- Male: body sides pale purplish pink with small rectangular golden spots forming seven longitudinal lines. Dorsal fin pale reddish brown with golden rays.

Fig. 120. *Campellolebias chrysolineatus*, wild male from type locality, about 25 mm SL, not preserved. Photo by the author.

Fig. 121. *Campellolebias brucei*, aquarium fish. Photo by Dr. B. Turner.

Caudal fin reddish with golden dots. *Female*: body sides pale brown with dark brown spots, often forming longitudinal rows. Unpaired fins hyaline with slight brown spots.

　Distribution.- Coastal lowlands between Barra do Saí and Itapema, Santa Catarina, southern Brazil.

Campellolebias brucei
Vaz-Ferreira & Sierra
(Fig. 121)

Campellolebias brucei Vaz-Ferreira & Sierra, 1974:1 (original description; annual puddle between Criciuma and Tubarão, Santa Catarina State, Brazil).
Cynolebias brucei; Parenti, 1981:491.
　Diagnosis.- Male with body sides crimson and longitudinal rows of green spots; 12 or 13 rays in posterior region of anal fin.
　Description.- Shape and position of fins as in *C. dorsimaculatus*. Males with 12 or 13 rays in posterior region of anal fin.
　Coloration.- *Male*: body sides crimson with seven longitudinal rows of drop-like green spots. Dorsal fin

pale reddish brown with green reflections. Caudal fin reddish with green dots. *Female*: body sides pale brown with dark brown spots, often forming longitudinal rows. Unpaired fins hyaline with slight brown spots.

　Distribution.- Coastal lowlands between Criciuma and Tubarão, Santa Catarina, southern Brazil.

　Remarks.- This species had not been collected again since 1972 (Costa, Lacerda & Brasil), but Dr. Gilberto Brasil recently (1988) found a new population near the type locality.

CYNOPOECILUS Regan

Cynopoecilus Regan, 1912:642 (type species *Cynolebias melanotaenia* Regan, 1912, by original designation).

　Diagnosis.- Eight minute and close rays connected to first proximal radial of anal fin; urohyal slender; body sides with broad horizontal black stripe; male and female with similar color patterns.
　Description.- Anal fin with eight minute and close rays connected to first proximal radial. Anal and dorsal

fins moderate in length. Length of anal fin base of male about 27.0% SL. Caudal fin of male somewhat truncate, length about 30% SL; about 35% of caudal scaled along longitudinal axis. Pectoral fins rounded, length about 20% SL. Pelvic fins with separated bases and six rays. Male and female with same number of dorsal fin rays. Urogenital papilla moderate. Branchiostegal membrane moderate. Male reaching about 30 mm SL.

Dorsal surface of head with scales neither reduced nor arranged in circular pattern. Mesial borders of anterocentral scales not overlapping. Anterior and posterior portions of supraorbital series of neuromasts united; anterior portion with seven or eight neuromasts; posterior portion with four or six aligned neuromasts. Neuromast on dermosphenotic

reduced. Preopercular canal absent.

Dentary moderate; dorsal and ventral surfaces not parallel. Ascending process of premaxilla narrow, without basal concavity. Vomer without teeth. Anguloarticular with anteromedian process moderate and anteroventral process reduced. Upper tip of quadrate without anterior expansion and posterior horizontal process moderate. Symplectic elongated. Mesopterygoid reduced. Upper tip of preopercle sharp and moderate.

Dermosphenotic absent. Lacrimal moderate, widened in upper portion and little twisted. Supraoccipital process horizontally oriented. Urohyal slender and with rounded posterodorsal tip. First epibranchial larger than second and third. Interarcual cartilage about 60% length

Fig. 122. *Cynopoecilus melanotaenia*, aquarium fish. H-J. Richter.

Fig. 123. *Cynopoecilus melanotaenia*, aquarium fish. Photo by K. Tanaka.

of second epibranchial. No molariform teeth in branchial apparatus. Basihyal short and somewhat broad. Proximal edge of first hypobranchial not bifid.

Twelve precaudal and 16 caudal vertebrae. First precaudal and caudal vertebrae without neural prezygapophysis. Proximal radials of anal fin narrow; second, third, and fourth not smaller than posterior proximal radials. Pectoral radials scale-like. Supracleithrum elongated. Lower tip of cleithrum without anterior expansion. Posttemporal without lower process.

Male and female with similar color patterns, characterized by broad longitudinal black stripe on body sides.

Male during courtship with unpaired fins erected and twisted. Fertilization external. Egg with reticulate surface and with mushroom-like prolongations. Egg diameter 0.9 mm. Development annual.

A single species is included: *C. melanotaenia.*

Distribution.- Coastal lowlands between southeastern Santa Catarina, southern Brazil, and northern Rocha, northeastern Uruguay (Fig. 101).

***Cynopoecilus melanotaenia* (Regan)**
(Figs. 122-123)

Cynolebias melanotaenia Regan, 1912a:506 (original description; Paranaguá, S.E. Brazil, locality corrected by Mayer, 1952 to Pelotas, Rio Grande do Sul, Brazil).
Cynopoecilus melanotaenia; Regan, 1912b:642.

Diagnosis.- As for the genus.
Description.- Dorsal and anal fins pointed. Posterior margin of pectoral fin reaches to anus in male and to base of pelvic fin in female. Pelvic fin reaches to anus. Origin of anal fin opposite dorsal fin rays 2-3.
Coloration.- Male and female with sides of body pale yellowish brown; broad longitudinal black stripe and another smaller one between pectoral fin base and anal fin origin. Dorsal and caudal fins with dark spots.
Distribution.- As for genus.

ECOLOGY

Except for the temporary character, no evident similarity can be pointed out as being common·to all the different known environments where the Cynolebiatinae live.

Fishes of the subfamily Cynolebiatinae are found from altitudes of about 1000 meters above sea level (*Cynolebias boitonei* in Brasília, central Brazil) to localities situated only a few meters from the sea (*Cynolebias constanciae* in Rio das Ostras, southeastern Brazil), both in extremely dry regions (*Cynolebias flavicaudatus* in northeastern Brazil) and areas of intense humidity (*Leptolebias sandrii* in southeastern Brazil). Equivalent discrepancies may be verified when comparing other data, such as pH and water temperature, as well as surrounding vegetation. However, each species often occurs only in one kind of environment.

Little is known about the habitat of *Millerichthys robustus* in Mexico. Nevertheless, the type locality of *M. robustus* is localized in a rain forest scattered about Middle America.

Terranatos dolichopterus occurs in northern South America, in a vast plain flooded by the Rio Orinoco, the Llanos Venezolanos. A llanos is a savannah area characterized by having few trees and abundant grass vegetation. *Terranatos dolichopterus* has been found in shaded environments with tea colored water at a depth between 1.0 and 1.5 meters, with values for pH and water temperature about 6.5 and 27°C respectively (Nico et al., 1987).

In northeastern South America may be found the Caatinga (Fig. 124), a semi-arid region where several *Cynolebias* species are found. Here shrubs, which are frequently armed with spines and deciduous during the dry season, are predominant. Except for the principal rivers, such as São Francisco and Parnaíba, the water courses often are temporary. In this region, Brasil (1973) recorded pH and water temperature values of about 7.0 and 28°C respectively in the habitat of *Cynolebias antenori* (Estado do Ceará).

The Chaco, a semi-arid region of central South America (including Bolivia, Paraguay, and Argentina at the western and southern Rio Paraguay basin), is similar to the Caatinga in appearance. The region is poor in rivers, which may have discontinuous courses. Some species of *Cynolebias* occur in "Chaco," but its habitats are not documented.

An ample savannah area called the Cerrado (Fig. 125) also occurs in central South America. In this area grasses are predominant, and trees with twisted shapes that rarely surpass six meters high, are very common. Annual fishes of the genera *Cynolebias*, *Maratecoara*, and *Plesiolebias* are found in Cerrado pools in which pH (6.4 - 8.5) and temperature (21 - 38°C) are rather variable (Bastos, 1984; Costa, Lacerda & Brasil, 1990; Lacerda, 1989).

Associated with the river margins and with trees reaching about 20 meters high, the gallery forests cross Cerrado and Caatinga areas. Two *Cynolebias* species, *C. zonatus* and *C. magnificus*, seem to be restricted to such shaded environments (Costa & Brasil, 1990; 1991).

Between the Cerrado and the Chaco is localized a large flooded region originating from the inundation of the courses of the middle and oriental Rio Paraguay basin during the wet season. The vegetation of this region, which is called the Pantanal (Figs. 126-127), is composed of floristic elements of

Fig. 124. Temporary flooded area in Caatinga, near Lagoa Grande, habitat of *Cynolebias flavicaudatus* and *C. porosus*. Photo by G. Brasil.

Fig. 125. Temporary swamp in Cerrado, near Nova Roma, habitat of *Cynolebias notatus*, *C. griseus*, and *C. flammeus*. Photo by G. Brasil.

Fig. 126. Temporary pool in Pantanal, near Miranda, habitat of *Plesiolebias bellus*. Photo by the author.

Fig. 127. Detail of temporary pool near Miranda. Photo by the author.

Cerrado and Chaco, besides Amazonian and eastern Brazilian forests. Some *Plesiolebias* species are found in this region (Costa, 1991; Costa & Lacerda, 1988a).

In the coastal flood plains of eastern Brazil, fishes of the subfamily Cynolebiatinae can occur both in coastal forests and in Restinga. In the coastal forests (Figs. 128-130), remaining from Atlantic forest, the humidity is intense and the arboreal stratum reaches 30 meters high. *Campellolebias* species and some *Leptolebias* are endemic to these areas. The water is extremely acid (pH 4.5 - 5.0) and the temperature moderate, not surpassing 25°C (Costa, Lacerda & Brasil, 1989; Lacerda & Ghisolfi, 1988).

In Restinga (Figs. 131-133) there is a large occurrence of xerophytes and banks of sand

Fig. 128 (left). Temporary flooded area in forest, near Magé, habitat of *Leptolebias sandrii*. Photo by the author.
Fig. 129 (below). Detail of temporary flooded area near Magé. Photo by the author.

are frequent in the scenery. In places of the most dense vegetation, the trees reach 4 m high. Like coastal forests, the water is very acid (pH 4.5 - 5.7) and the temperature is pleasant (20 - 27°C) (Costa, Lacerda & Tanizaki, 1988b). Some species of *Cynolebias* and *Leptolebias* occur in these places.

In the plains around the lower Plata and Uruguay basins, the open areas called Pampas are predominant. Species of *Cynolebias* and *Cynopoecilus* occur in the cold (10 -21°C) and acid (pH 6.1 - 6.4) waters of this region (Lüling, 1982).

Data regarding trophic relationships between fishes of the subfamily Cynolebiatinae and other organisms are very scanty. Thomerson & Taphorn (1987) reported *Terranatos dolichopterus* eating copepods, but feeding

Fig. 130 (above). Detail of a temporary puddle in a forest, near Paranaguá, habitat of *Leptolebias aureoguttatus.* Photo by the author.

Fig. 131 (right). Temporary lagoon in Restinga, near Maricá, habitat of *Leptolebias fluminensis.* Photo by the author.

habits of other species of the Cynolebiatinae in nature are completely unknown.

In Rio das Ostras, *Cynolebias constanciae*, *C. whitei*, and *Leptolebias cruzi* may be found in the same pond. *Cynolebias whitei*, abundant in neighborhoods where it is the only fish, is very rare in that place. The study of stomach contents of the two abundant species in Rio das Ostras, *C. constanciae* and *L. cruzi*, revealed that they ingest the same food items, but in different proportions (Tab. 3). There is a clear preference for rotifers and little crustaceans in *L. cruzi*, while *C. constanciae* eats crustaceans and aquatic insect larvae in equal proportions and rarely ingests rotifers.

Fig. 132. Detail of temporary pond near Barra de São João. Photo by the author.

Fig. 133. Temporary pond in Restinga, near Barra de São João, habitat of *Cynolebias constanciae*, *C. whitei*, and *Leptolebias cruzi*. Photo by the author.

BIOGEOGRAPHY

Biogeographic analysis of Neotropical fishes has been the focus of several recent studies. These may be classified into three groups according to their approaches. The first group includes works focusing on similarities of ichthyofaunistic composition from different basins, defining areas of endemism (for a review of these studies, see Weitzman & Weitzman, 1982).

In the second group are works dedicated to discussions about distribution pattern origin of allopatric species of a given monophyletic group, based on geological data (e.g., Kullander, 1983; Menezes, 1988).

In the third category, the works attempt to relate phylogenetic results with the distribution of included taxa (e.g., Parenti, 1981; Weitzman & Fink, 1985; Weitzman et al., 1988; Vari, 1988). Under such a perspective, it is assumed that the whole area occupied by all taxa of a monophyletic group was occupied in the past by an ancestral species. The number of recent taxa and the levels of relationships among them correspond to the different stages of barrier appearances within the ancestral area, and the consequent isolation of ancestral species portions.

For such a proposal, hierarchies of relationships among organisms (cladograms) are converted into hierarchies of historical relationships among areas (cladograms of areas). Such methodology, so called "vicariance biogeography" and first expounded by Platnick & Nelson (1978), presents a notable advantage among approaches in historical biogeography because it allows the proposition of objective and potentially falsifiable hypotheses (widely discussed by Nelson & Platnick, 1981).

Still under this biogeographic perspective the reduced vagility of freshwater organisms provide excellent opportunities for studies of historical patterns due to the isolation in the countless Neotropical basins (Vari, 1988). Annual fishes are highly promising because they live exclusively in temporary environments and the eggs need a dry stage to complete their development. Hence, both elevations of non-flooded terrains and any perennial water course form barriers to annual fish populations.

Based on a phylogenetic analysis of the genera of the family Rivulidae, Parenti (1981) proposed a cladogram of areas and discussed the pattern found. However, Parenti's phylogenetic analysis of rivulid genera was not supported by subsequent studies (Costa, 1988b; 1989; 1990a) and the areas defined by Parenti in South America were somewhat inaccurate. Thus, in Parenti's analysis, *Cynolebias* (=Cynolebiatinae in the present study), *Trigonectes* Myers, 1925, and *Neofundulus* Myers, 1924 were reported as occurring in the South, and *Pterolebias* Garman, 1895 in the North. However, *Trigonectes* and *Neofundulus* are in fact distributed in the Middle and *Cynolebias* (sensu Parenti) in the Northeast, Middle, and Southeast.

According to the basic procedures of the vicariance biogeography methodology, the cladogram of phylogenetic relationships of Cynolebiatinae (Fig. 13) yields the cladogram of areas of Fig. 134A. These areas are delimited through the distribution of monophyletic assemblages of Cynolebiatinae and other Neotropical freshwater fishes (Fig. 135). In spite of the easy distinction between the nine areas of endemism, small overlapping areas may be observed in Araguaia, Paraguay, and eastern isolated basins.

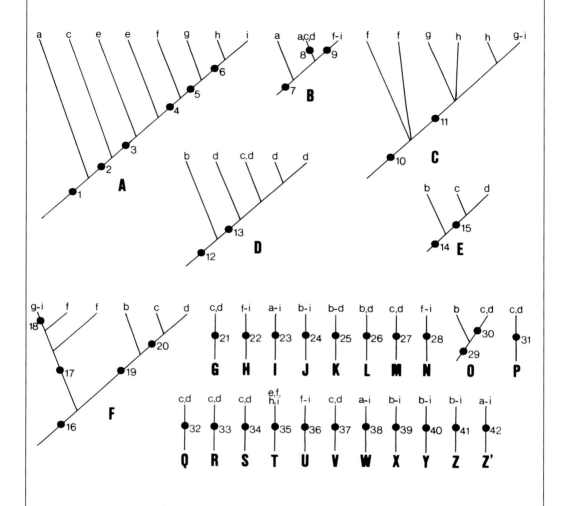

Fig. 134. Distribution patterns of some representatives of Neotropical faunal areas of endemism (a-i): A = Cynolebiatinae; B = Anablepidae; C = *Mimagoniates*; D = *Potamorhina*; E = *Curimata*, clade *mivarti-cesarina-aspera*; F = *Ceratophrys*; G = *Lebistes* (subgenus of *Poecilia*); H = Cnesterodontini; I = Rivulinae; J = Erythrinidae; K = Gasteropelecidae; L = Xenurobryconini; M = *Curimatopsis*; N = *Oligosarcus*; O = *Abramites*; P = *Cichla*; Q = *Astronotus*; R = *Mesonauta*; S = *Heros*; T = *Gymnogeophagus*; U = *Geophagus brasiliensis*; V = *Electrophorus*; W = *Gymnotus*; X = Loricariidae; Y = Trichomycteridae; Z = Callichthyidae; Z' = *Synbranchus*.

The occurrence of a monophyletic group broadly distributed in Middle and South America, suggests that there was in the past an ancestral species distributed in the whole area now occupied by its descendants. This may have taken place in the Cretaceous, before the total split between the South American and African plates, when the actual Neotropical region was constituted by vast plains (Beurlen, 1970), without prominent barriers between the areas of endemism delimited in the present study.

The Cynolebiatinae are missing in the Amazonian region. This fact may be due to the scarceness of collecting data, but other annual fishes have been reported in this region. Species of the annual genera *Moema* Costa, 1989, and *Pterolebias* Garman, 1895, occur in several Amazonian localities (Costa, 1988c, 1989, 1993; Seegers, 1983; 1984; 1987). Also the non annual genus *Rivulus* Poey, 1860, is widely represented in the Amazon region (Costa, 1990d, 1992; Fels & de Rham, 1982). Representatives of these genera (*Moema*, *Pterolebias*, and *Rivulus*) have been found associated with species of the

Cynolebiatinae in other regions (Taphorn & Thomerson, 1975; Costa & Lacerda, 1988a), which suggests that the absence of Cynolebiatinae in the Amazonian region is not due to collecting scarcity. Nevertheless, it is not clear if this is a consequence of geological or ecological factors. The Cynolebiatinae also are missing in the Trans-Andean region.

Four main factors impede adequate comparisons between biogeographic patterns obtained in Cynolebiatinae

Fig. 135. Areas of endemism delimited according to distribution patterns of monophyletic groups of Neotropical fishes.

phylogeny and patterns exhibited by other freshwater fishes: 1) the scarcity of recent taxonomic studies at the species level; 2) the scarceness of phylogenetic studies; 3) the large occurrence of widespread taxa in studied groups, and 4) the non-overlapping of involved areas in different studies. However, some similarities between the Cynolebiatinae and other distribution patterns of clearly monophyletic groups of fishes and a frog genus may be pointed out. Phylogenetic studies of the cyprinodontiform family Anablepidae (Parenti, 1981), the characiform genera *Mimagoniates* Regan (Menezes & Weitzman, 1990), *Potamorhina* Cope (Vari, 1984), and *Curimata* Bosc (clade *mivarti-cesarina-aspera* in Vari, 1988), and the leptodactylid genus *Ceratophrys* (Lynch, 1982), may be approximately converted in the cladograms of areas of Figure 134B-F. Additionally, distributional data for monophyletic groups of Neotropical fishes such as the cyprinodontiform subgenus *Lebistes* Filippi, tribe

Cnesterodontini, and subfamily Rivulinae, the characiform families Erythrinidae and Gasteropelecidae, tribe Xenurobryconini (according to Weitzman & Fink, 1985), and genera *Curimatopsis* Steindachner (according to Vari, 1982), *Oligosarcus* Günther (according to Menezes, 1988), and *Abramites* Fowler (according to Vari & Williams, 1987), the cichlid genera *Cichla* Schneider, *Astronotus* Swainson, *Mesonauta* Günther, *Heros* Heckel, *Gymnogeophagus* Ribeiro (according to Reis & Malabarba, 1988), and the species *Geophagus brasiliensis* (Quoy & Gaimard), the gymnotoid genera *Electrophorus* Linnaeus and *Gymnotus* Linnaeus, the siluriform families Loricariidae, Trichomycteridae, and Callichthyidae, and the synbranchiform genus *Synbranchus* Bloch, provide other comparative support (Fig. 134G-Z'). Following the methodology of *Biogeographic Parsimony Analysis*, all cladograms of Figure 134 yield a single cladogram of area (Fig. 136), which represents a biogeographic historical hypothesis for the Neotropical region.

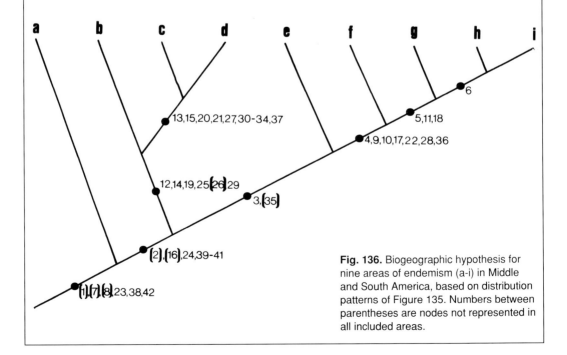

Fig. 136. Biogeographic hypothesis for nine areas of endemism (a-i) in Middle and South America, based on distribution patterns of Figure 135. Numbers between parentheses are nodes not represented in all included areas.

REFERENCES

Ahl, E. 1922. Die Gattung *Cynolebias*. *Blatt. Aquar. Terr'kunde*, 33(14):221-225.

Ahl, E. 1924. Uber einige neue Fische aus Sudamerika. *Zool. Anz.*, 58:358-359.

Ahl, E. 1934. Eine Revision der Zahnkarpfengattung *Cynolebias*. *Zool. Anz.*, 108:304-310.

Ahl, E. 1938. Beschreibung neuer Zahnkarpfen aus dem Zoologischen Museum Berlin. *Zool. Anz.*, 1924:53-58.

Amato, L. H. 1986. Seis especies nuevas del genero *Cynolebias* Steindachner, 1876, de Uruguay y Paraguay (Cyprinodontiformes, Rivulidae). *Com. Zool. Mus. Hist. Nat. Montevideo*, 11(162):1-27.

Amato, L. H. 1987. Descripcion de *Cynolebias cyaneus* n. sp., nuevo pez anual del Estado de Rio Grande do Sul, Brasil (Cyprinodontiformes, Rivulidae). *Com. Zool. Mus. Hist. Nat. Montevideo*, 11(163):1-11.

Bastos, E. K. 1984. *Cynolebias boitonei*, in Zentral-Brasilien beobachtet. *Das Aquarium*, 18:119-123.

Berg, C. 1897. Contribuciones al conocimiento de los peces sudamericanos, especialmente de la Republica Argentina. *Anal. Mus. Nac. Buenos Aires, ser. 2*, 2(5):263-302.

Berkenkamp, H.O. 1993. Ein neuer Fächerfisch aus dem Bundesstaat Minas Gerais, Brasilien. *Das Aquar.*, 290:8-15.

Beurlen, K. 1970. *Geologie von Brasilien*. Gebruder Borntraeger, Berlin.

Böhlke, J. E., S. H. Weitzman & N. A. Menezes. 1978. Estado atual da sistemática de peixes de água doce da América do Sul. *Acta Amazonica*, 8(4):657-677.

Brasil, G. C. 1973. A new *Cynolebias* from northeastern Brazil. *Aquar. Digest Internat.*, 2(2):3-4.

Brooks, D. R. 1981. Hennig's parasitological method: A proposed solution. *Syst. Zool.*, 30:229-249.

Carvalho, A. L. 1957. Notas para o conhecimento da biologia dos peixes anuais. *Rev. Bras. Biol.*, 17(4):459-466.

Carvalho, A. L. 1959. Novo gênero e nova espécie de peixe anual de Brasília, com uma nota sobre os peixes anuais da Baixada Fluminense, Brasil. *Bol. Mus. Nac. Rio de Janeiro*, 201:1-10.

Carvalho, A. L. 1971. Um novo peixe anual do Estado do Espírito Santo (Pisces, Cyprinodontidae, Rivulinae). *Rev. Bras. Biol.*, 31(3):401-404.

Carvalho, A. L. & C. A. G. Cruz. 1987. Um novo *Cynolebias* do Sudeste Baiano (Pisces, Cyprinodontidae, Rivulinae). *Arq. Univ. Fed. Rur. Rio de Janeiro*, 8(1):11-15.

Castello, H. P. & R. B. Lopez. 1974. *Cynolebias alexandri*, a new species of annual killifish from Argentina, with notes on *C. bellottii*. *Trop. Fish. Hobby.*, 23(9):34-42.

Costa, W. J. E. M. 1988a. Sistemática e distribuição do complexo de espécies *Cynolebias minimus* (Cyprinodontiformes, Rivulidae), com a descrição de duas espécies novas. *Rev. Brasil. Zool.*, 5(4):557-570.

Costa, W. J. E. M. 1988b. Sistemática e distribuição do gênero *Neofundulus* (Cyprinodontiformes, Rivulidae). *Rev. Brasil. Biol.*, 48(1):103-111.

Costa, W. J. E. M. 1988c. A new species of the neotropical annual fish genus *Pterolebias* (Cyprinodontiformes, Rivulidae), from Central Brazil. *J. Zool.*,

215(5):657-661.

Costa, W. J. E. M. 1989. Descrição e relações filogenéticas de dois gêneros novos e três espécies novas de peixes anuais neotropicais (Cyprinodontiformes, Rivulidae). *Rev. Brasil. Biol.*, 49(1):221-230.

Costa, W. J. E. M. 1990a. Análise filogenética da família Rivulidae (Cyprinodontiformes, Aplocheiloidei). *Rev. Brasil. Biol.*, 50(1):65-82.

Costa, W. J. E. M. 1990b. Redescrição do gênero *Cynolebias* (Cyprinodontiformes, Rivulidae), com a descrição de uma nova espécie da bacia do rio Tocantins. *Comum. Mus. Ciênc. PUCRS, ser. zool.*, 2(9):181-190.

Costa, W. J. E. M. 1990c. Descrição de um gênero e duas espécies novas de peixes anuais do centro da América do Sul (Cyprinodontiformes, Rivulidae). *Comum. Mus. Ciênc. PUCRS, ser. zool.*, 2(9):191-202.

Costa, W. J. E. M. 1990d. Description d'une nouvelle espece du genre *Rivulus* (Cyprinodontiformes, Rivulidae) de l'Amazone orientale. *Rev. fr. aquariol.*, 17(2):41-44.

Costa, W. J. E. M. 1991. Systematics and distribution of the neotropical annual fish genus *Plesiolebias* (Cyprinodontiformes : Rivulidae), with description of a new species. *Ichthyol. Explor. Freshwaters*, 1(4):369-378.

Costa, W. J. E. M. 1992. Redescrição do gênero *Rivulus* (Cyprinodontiformes, Rivulidae), com a descrição de duas novas espécies do Brasil Central. *Rev. Brasil. Biol.*, 51(2):327-333.

Costa, W. J. E. M. 1993a. Sistemática e distribuição do gênero *Moema* (Cyprinodontiformes: Rivulidae), com a descrição de uma nova espécie. *Rev. Brasil. Biol.*, 52(4):619-625.

Costa, W. J. E. M. & G. C. Brasil.

1990. Description of two new annual fishes of the genus *Cynolebias* (Cyprinodontiformes: Rivulidae) from the São Francisco basin, Brazil. *Ichthyol. Explor. Freshwaters*, 1(1):15-22.

Costa, W. J. E. M. & G. C. Brasil. 1991. Three new species of *Cynolebias* (Cyprinodontiformes: Rivulidae) from the São Francisco basin, Brazil. *Ichthyol. Explor. Freshwaters*, 2(1):55-62.

Costa, W. J. E. M. & G. C. Brasil. 1993. Two new species of *Cynolebias* (Cyprinodontiformes: Rivulidae) from the São Francisco basin, Brazil, with notes on phylogeny and biogeography of annual fishes. *Ichthyol. Explor. Freshwaters*, 4(3):199-200.

Costa, W. J. E. M. & M. T. C. Lacerda. 1988a. Descrição de uma nova espécie de peixe anual do gênero *Cynolebias* do Brasil Central (Cyprinodontiformes, Rivulidae). *Rev. Aquariof.*, 5:16-20.

Costa, W. J. E. M. & M. T. C. Lacerda. 1988b. Identité et redescription de *Cynolebias sandrii* et de *Cynolebias fluminensis* (Cyprinodontiformes, Rivulidae). *Rev. fr. Aquariol.*, 14(4):127-132.

Costa, W. J. E. M., M. T. C. Lacerda & G. C. Brasil. 1989. Systématique et distribution du genre néotropical *Campellolebias* (Cyprinodontiformes, Rivulidae), avec description de deux nouvelles especes. *Rev. fr. Aquariol.*, 15(3):65-72.

Costa, W. J. E. M., M. T. C. Lacerda & G. C. Brasil. 1990. Description de deux nouvelles especes du genre *Cynolebias* du bassin du Rio Tocantins (Cyprinodontiformes, Rivulidae). Rev. fr. Aquariol., 17(1):9-14.

Costa, W. J. E. M., M. T. C. Lacerda & K. Tanizaki. 1988a. Description d'une nouvelle espece de *Cynolebias* du Brésil central (Cyprinodontiformes, Rivulidae). *Rev. fr. Aquariol.*, 14(4):123-126.

Costa, W. J. E. M., M. T. C. Lacerda & K. Tanizaki. 1988b. Description d'une nouvelle espece de *Cynolebias* des plaines côtieres du Brésil sud-oriental (Cyprinodontiformes, Rivulidae). *Rev. fr. Aquariol.*, 15(1):21-24.

Cruz, C. A. G. 1974. Sobre *Cynolebias aureoguttatus* Myers, 1952 (Osteichthyes, Cyprinodontidae, Rivulinae). *Arq. Univ. Fed. Rur. Rio de Janeiro*, 2(4):19-21.

Cruz, C. A. G. 1983. Uma nova espécie de *Cynolebias* do Estado do Espírito Santo, Brasil (Pisces, Cyprinodontidae). *Pap. Avul. Zool.*, 35(6):73-77.

Cruz, C. A. G. & O. L. Peixoto. 1985. Novo Peixe anual do Estado do Rio de Janeiro, Brasil (Pisces, Cyprinodontidae). *Arq. Univ. Rur. Rio de Janeiro*, 6(1):89-93.

Cruz, C. A. G. & O. L. Peixoto. 1992. Descrição de uma nova espécie de peixe anual do Estado da Buhia, Brasil (Cyprinodontiformes, Rivulidae). *Rev. Brasil. Zool.*, 7(4):637-641.

Dingerkus, G. & L. D. Uhler. 1977. Enzyme clearing alcian blue stained whole small vertebrates for demonstration of cartilage. *Stain Tech.*, 52(4):229-232.

Faria, A. & H. Muller. 1937. Espécies da família Cyprinodontidae, gênero *Cynopoecilus*, constatadas em águas do Brasil. *Rev. Naval*, 1934(3):98-99.

Farris, J. S. 1983. The logical basis of phylogenetic analysis. *In*: Platnick, N. I. & A. Funk. (eds). Advances in cladistics. *Proc. 2nd meeting W. Hennig Soc.*, pp:7-36. Columbia Univ. Press, New York.

Fels, J. F. & P. de Rham. 1982. Récentes collections de *Rivulus* (Cyprinodontiformes) au Peru, avec description de six nouvelles especes (2). *Rev. fr. Aquariol.*, 8:97-106.

Foersch, W. 1958. Beobachtungen und Erfahrungen bei der Pflege und Zucht von *Cynolebias ladigesi* Myers. *Aquar. Terr. Zeit. (DATZ)*, 11(9):257-260.

Garman, S. 1985. The cyprinodonts. *Mem. Mus. Comp. Zool. Harvard*, 19(1):1-179.

Günther, A. 1883. On a new species of *Cynolebias* from the Argentine Republic. *Ann. & Mag. Nat. Hist.*, ser. 5, 11:140-141.

Hennig, W. 1950. *Grunzuge einer Theorie der phylogenetischen Systematik*. Deutscher Zentralverlag, Berlin.

Hoedeman, J. J. 1960. Studies on cyprinodontiform fishes 10. On the probable evolution of the frontal scalation pattern. *Bull. Aquatic Biol.*, 2(18):82-92.

Huber, J. H. 1981. *Cynolebias heloplites* n. sp. *Supp. Killi Rev.*, 5:1-15.

Ihering, R. 1931. Cyprinodontes brasileiros. *Arc. Inst. Biol.*, 4:243-280.

Kullander, S. O. 1983. *A revision of the South American cichlid genus Cichlasoma (Teleostei: Cichlidae)*. Naturhistoriska Riksmusset, Stockholm.

Lacerda, M. T. C. 1987. Comentários sobre as espécies de *Cynolebias* incluidas na lista dos peixes ameaçados de extinção. *Rev. Aquariof.*, 3:34-36.

Lacerda, M. T. C. 1989. Araguaia: em busca de *Cynolebias* GO-3. *Rev. Aquariof.*, 9:20-29.

Lacerda, M. T. C. & J. C. Ghisolfi. *Cynolebias aureoguttatus* Cruz, 1974, ein Waldbewohner. *Deutsche Killifisch Gemein., J.*, 20(4):55-63.

Ladiges, W. 1934. *Cynopoecilus marmoratus* Ladiges. *Das Aquarium*, 1934:73-74.

Ladiges, W. 1955. Neue fische aus

Zentral-Brasilien. *Aquar. Terr. Zeit. (DATZ)*, 8(9):230-232.

Ladiges, W. 1958. Eine vierte, neue Art der Gattung *Pterolebias* von Cabo Frio, Rio de Janeiro. *Aquar. Terr. Zeit. (DATZ)*, 11(3):76-77.

Lazara, K. J. 1991. *Cynolebias lacortei, Cynolebias costai,* and *Cynolebias aruana* -Three new species of cloud fish from Brazil. *J. Am. Killifish Assoc.*, 23(4):139-152.

Lüling, K. H. 1982. Wissenschaftliche Ergebnisse der Uruguay-Argentinien-Expedition Dr. K.H. Lüling 1979. II. Uber die Biotop von *Cynolebias viarius* und *Cynolebias melanotaenia* (Pisces, Cyprinodontidae) und ihre Begleitfische in Osturuguay. *Zool. Beitr.*, 27(2/3):297-311.

Lynch, J. D. 1982. Relationships of the frogs of the genus *Ceratophrys* (Leptodactylidae) and their bearing on hypotheses of Pleistocene forest refugia on South America and punctuated equilibria. *Syst. Zool.*, 31(3):166-179.

Maddison, W. P., M. J. Donoghue & D.R. Maddison. 1984. Outgroup analysis and parsimony. *Syst. Zool.*, 33:83-103.

Mayer, F. 1952. A rare aquarium fish from Brazil, *Cynolebias melanotaenia. The Aquarium J.*, 23:114-115.

Menezes, N. A. 1988. Implications of the distribution patterns of the species of *Oligosarcus* (Teleostei, Characidae) from Central and Southern South America, pp. 295-304, *In* Vanzolini, P.E., and W.R. Heyer (editors). Neotropical distribution patterns: Proceedings of a workshop. *Academia Brasileira de Ciências, Rio de Janeiro.*

Menezes, N. A. & S. H. Weitzman. 1990. Two new species of *Mimagoniates* (Teleostei: Characidae: Glandulocaudinae), their phylogeny and biogeography and a key to the Glandulocaudin fishes of Brazil and Paraguay. *Proc. Biol. Soc. Wash.*, 103(2):380-426.

Miller, R. R. & C. L. Hubbs. 1974. *Rivulus robustus,* a new cyprinodontid fish from southeastern Mexico. *Copeia,* 1974:865-869.

Myers, G. S. 1942. Studies on South American freshwater fishes I. *Stan. Ichth. Bull.*, 2(4):89-114.

Myers, G. S. 1944. Field-notes on fishes of the vicinity of Rio de Janeiro. *The Aquarium,* 1944(2):185-206.

Myers, G. S. 1947. The Amazon and its fishes. Part 4. The fish in its environment. *Aquar. J.*, 18:8-19.

Myers, G. S. 1952. Annual fishes. *Aquar. J.*, 23:125-141.

Nelson, G. & N. Platnick. 1981. *Systematics and Biogeography: Cladistics and Vicariance.* Columbia University Press, New York.

Nico, L. G., D. C. Taphorn & J. E. Thomerson. 1987. Datos limnologicos sobre el habitat de los peces anuales (Cyprinodontidae) de los Llanos Venezolanos con una clave para su identificacion. *BioLlania,* 5:129-144.

Parenti, L. R. 1981. A phylogenetic and biogeographic analysis of cyprinodontiform fishes (Teleostei, Atherinomorpha). *Bull. Amer. Mus. Nat. Hist.*, 168(4):335-557.

Perugia, A. 1891. Appunti sopra alcuni pesci Sud-Americani. *Ann. Mus. Civ. Storia Natur. Genova, ser. 2,* 10:605-657.

Peters, F. & L. Seegers. 1978. Ein fisch ohne Bauchflossen-*Cynolebias boitonei. Aquarien Mag.*, 12(8):390-394.

Platnick, N. & G. Nelson. 1978. A method of analysis for historical biogeography. *Syst. Zool.*, 27(1):1-16.

Regan, C.T. 1912a. A revision of the poeciliid fishes of the genera

Rivulus, Pterolebias, and *Cynolebias. Ann. & Mag. Nat. Hist., ser. 8*, 10:494-508.

Regan, C. T. 1912b. Sexual differences in the poeciliid fishes of the genus *Cynolebias. Ann. & Mag. Nat. Hist., ser. 8*, 10:641-642.

Reichert, J.J. 1992. Ein neuer *Cynolebias*-Fundort in Uruguay *DKG-Journal*, 24(4):58-60.

Reis, R. E. & L. R. Malabarba. 1988. Revision of the neotropical cichlid genus *Gymnogeophagus* Ribeiro, 1918, with descriptions of two new species (Pisces, Perciformes). *Rev. Brasil. Zool.*, 4(4):259-305.

Ribeiro, A. M. 1939. Alguns novos dados ictiológicos da nossa fauna. *Bol. Biol.*, 4(3):358-363.

Ringuellet, R. A., R. H. Aramburu & A. A. Aramburu. 1967. *Los peces Argentinos de agua dulce*. Comission de Investigación científica, La Plata.

Rosen, D. E. 1978. Vicariant patterns and historical explanation of biogeography. *Syst. Zool.*, 27(2):159-188.

Schreitmuller, W. 1937. Neue Susswasserfische. *Das Aquarium*, ?:11-14.

Schroeter, L. 1956. *Cynolebias (Cynopoecilus) splendens* Myers - ein neuer farbenprachtiger Aquarienfisch aus Brasilien. *Die Aquar. und Terrar. Zeit. (DATZ)*, 9(3):63-66.

Seegers, L. 1983. *Pterolebias wischmanni* nov. spec. aus dem Ucayali-Einzug in Peru (Pisces: Atheriniformes: Rivulinae). *Deutsche Killifisch Gemein. J.*, 15(5):67-74.

Seegers, L. 1984. Ein neuer Rivuline aus Peru: *Pterolebias rubrocaudatus* (Pisces: Atheriniformes: Cyprinodontidae). *Bonn. zool. Beitr.*, 35(1-3):243-250.

Seegers, L. 1987. Die gattung *Pterolebias* Garman 1895 mit der beschreibung von *Pterolebias staecki* nov. spec. *Die Aquar. und Terrar. Zeit. (DATZ)*, 40(5):199-204.

Seegers, L. 1980. *Killifische, eierlegende Zahnkarpfen im Aquarium*. Verlag Eugen Ulmer, Stuttgart.

Seegers, L. 1988. Ein neuer Facherkaepfling aus dem brasilianischen Pantanal—*Cynolebias pantanalensis* n. sp. (Cyprinodontiformes: Rivulidae). *Die Aquar. und Terrar. Zeitschrift (DATZ)*, 41(4):30-33.

Stansch, K. 1908. Einiges uber *Haplochilus*-Arten und -Varietaten. *Wochen. Aquar. Terr'kunde*, 5(7):77-79.

Steindachner, F. 1876. Ichthyologische Beitrage (V). *Sitz. Akad. Wiss. Wien mathem. -naturw. Klasse Abt. 1*, 74:49-240.

Steindachner, F. 1881. Sitzung der mathematisch-naturwissenschaftlichen. *Anz. Akad. Wiss. Wien*, 18:97-100.

Taberner, R., J. O. F. Santos & J. O. Castelli. 1974. Datos para conocimiento de *Cynolebias nonoiuliensis* sp. nov. (Pisces, Cyprinodontidae). *Physis, ser. B*, 33(87):187-193.

Taphorn, D. C. & J. E. Thomerson. 1975. Annual killifishes of the Orinoco basin of Venezuela. *J. Am. Killifish Assoc.*, 10:1-7.

Taphorn, D. C. & J. E. Thomerson. 1978. A revision of the South American cyprinodont fishes of the genera *Rachovia* and *Austrofundulus*, with the description of a new genus. *Acta Biol. Venezuela*, 9(4):377-452.

Tulipano, J. 1973. *Cynolebias antenori. Killie notes Amer. Killifish Assoc.*, 6(11):23-24.

Vari, R. P. 1982. Systematics of the neotropical characoid genus *Curimatopsis* (Pisces: Characoidei). *Smithsonian Contrib. Zool.* 373:1-28.

Vari, R. P. 1984. Systematics of the neotropical characiform genus

Potamorhina (Pisces: Characiformes). *Smithsonian Contrib. Zool.*, 400:1-36.

Vari, R. P. 1988. The Curimatidae, a lowland neotropical fish family (Pisces: Characiformes); distribution, endemism, and phylogenetic biogeography, pp. 313-348, in Vanzolini, P.E., and W.R. Heyer (editors). Neotropical distribution patterns: Proceedings of a workshop. *Academia Brasileira de Ciências, Rio de Janeiro.*

Vari, R. P. & A. M. Williams. 1987. Headstanders of the neotropical anostomid genus *Abramites* (Pisces: Characiformes: Anostomidae). *Proc. Biol. Soc. Washington*, 100(1):89-103.

Vaz-Ferreira, R. & A. R. Melgarejo. 1984. La distribucion de las especies del genero *Cynolebias* Steindachner, 1876, en el Uruguay, con notas sobre *C. alexandri* Castello y Lopez, 1974. *Bol. Soc. Zool. Uruguay*, 2:41-45.

Vaz-Ferreira, R. & B. Sierra. 1971. Especies del genero *Cynolebias* Steindachner, 1876 en el Uruguay. *Bol. Soc. Zool. Uruguay*, 1:24-44.

Vaz-Ferreira, R. & B. Sierra. 1972. Caracteres etologicos genericos y especificos en los peces del genero *Cynolebias* Steindachner, 1876. *Bol. Soc. Zool. Uruguay*, 2:22-35.

Vaz-Ferreira, R. & B. Sierra. 1973. El genero *Cynolebias* Steindachner, 1876 (Atheriniformes, Cyprinodontidae): caracteres, especies y distribucion. *Trab. V Congr. Latinoamer. Zool.*, 1:245-260.

Vaz-Ferreira, R. & B. Sierra. 1974. *Campellolebias brucei* n. gen. n. sp., cyprinodontido con especializacion de la papila genital y de los primeros radios de la aleta anal. *Com. Zool. Mus. Hist. Nat. Montevideo,*

138(10):1-17.

Vaz-Ferreira, R., B. Sierra & S. S. Paulete. 1964. Tres especies nuevas del genero *Cynolebias* Steindachner, 1876 (Teleostomi, Cyprinodontidae). *Com. Zool. Mus. Hist. Nat. Montevideo,* 8(102):1-36.

Weitzman, S. H. & S. V. Fink. 1985. Xenurobryconin phylogeny and putative pheromone pumps in Glandulocaudine fishes (Teleostei: Characidae). *Smithsonian Contributions to Zoology*, 421:1-121.

Weitzman, S. H., N. A. Menezes, and M. J. Weitzman. 1988. Phylogenetic biogeography of the Glandulocaudini (Teleostei: Characiformes, Characidae) with comments on the distributions of other freshwater fishes in Eastern and Southeastern Brazil, pp. 379-427, *In* Vanzolini, P. E., and W. R. Heyer (editors). Neotropical distribution patterns: Proceedings of a workshop. *Academia Brasileira de Ciências, Rio de Janeiro.*

Weitzman, S. H & M. J. Weitzman. 1982. Biogeography and evolutionary diversification in neotropical freshwater fishes with comments on the refuge theory, pp. 403-422, *In* G. Prance (Editor). *Biological diversification in the tropics.* Columbia University Press, New York.

Weitzman, S. H. & J. P. Wourms. 1967. South American cyprinodont fishes allied to *Cynolebias* with the description of a new species of *Austrofundulus* from Venezuela. *Copeia*, 1967:89-100.

Wildekamp, R. 1981. *Pracht-karpflinge.* Kernen Verlag, Essen.

Wiley, E. O. 1981. *Phylogenetics: the theory and practice of phylogenetic systematics.* John Wiley, New York

APPENDIX

The material examined in the present study is deposited in the following institutions: California Academy of Sciences, San Francisco (SU, formerly in Stanford University); Facultad de Humanidades y Ciencias, Depto. Zoología de Vertebrados, Montevideo (ZVC.P); Museu de Ciências, Pontífica Universidade Católica do Rio Grande do Sul, Porto Alegre (MCP); Museo Nacional de Historia Natural, Montevideo (MHNM); Museu Nacional do Rio de Janeiro (MNRJ); Museu de Zoologia da Universidade de São Paulo (MZUSP); Universidade Federal do Rio de Janeiro (UFRJ); Universidade Federal Rural do Rio de Janeiro, collection of Carlos Cruz (CAGC); University of Michigan, Museum of Zoology, Ann Arbor (UMMZ); Zoologisch Museum Amsterdam (ZMA). The material is listed below, except for uncataloged and not preserved examples. Asterisk means cleared and stained specimens.

Campellolebias brucei - ZVC, P. 2126, 1 paratype; ZVC, P. 2127, 1 paratype; Brazil: Santa Catarina: Criciuma-Tubarão road; G.C.Brasil, 28 XI 1972. - UFRJ 293, 11 ex.; Brazil: Santa Catarina: Tubarão; G.C.Brasil, VIII 1988.

Campellolebias chrysolineatus - MZUSP 38817, holotype; MZUSP 38818, 2 paratypes; MZUSP 38819, 1 paratype; MNRJ 11494, 2 paratypes; Brazil: Santa Catarina: Araquari; M.T.C.Lacerda, G.C.Brasil, G.C.Ghisolfi & V.Franciozi, 21 XI 1987. - MZUSP 38344, 11 paratypes; MZUSP 38428, 2 ex. (*); idem; C.Tatsuta, V.Teixeira, C.Gastaldi & V.Franciozi, IV 1986. - UFRJ 284, 2 ex.;Brazil: Santa Catarina: Itapema; G.C.Brasil, 19 VIII 1988.

Campellolebias dorsimaculatus - MZUSP 38813, holotype; MZUSP 38816, 1 paratype; MZUSP 38815, 12 paratypes; Brazil: São Paulo: Iguape; G.C.Brasil & D.Nielsen, 31 III 1988. - MZUSP 38816, 9 paratypes; MNRJ 11493, 2 paratypes; idem; G.C.Brasil & D.Nielsen, 19 VII 1988.

Cynolebias adloffi - MNRJ 11393, 2 ex.; Brazil: Rio Grande do Sul: São Leopoldo; T. Lacerda, 18 X 1967. - MNRJ 9749, 8 ex.; Brazil: Rio Grande do Sul: Pueblo Niteroi; R. Vaz-Ferreira, B.S.Soriano & J.Soriano, 8 XI 1962. - MNRJ 11375, 2 ex.; Brazil: Rio Grande do Sul: Rio Grande; B.N.Barcelos, 4 X 1955. - MZUSP 4493, 22 ex.; MZUSP 38458, 1 ex. (*); MZUSP 4494, 20 ex.; Brazil: Rio Grande do Sul: Pelotas; Expedição Departamento de Zoologia, 22 VIII 1966. - MZUSP 41011, 8 ex.; Brazil: Rio Grande do Sul: Alvorada; Malabarba, Reis, Bergmann & Azevedo, 9 VII 1986. - MZUSP 38411, 8 ex.; Brazil: Rio Grande do Sul: Porto Alegre; VI 1986. - MZUSP 38376, 9 ex.; Brazil: Rio Grande do Sul: São Leopoldo; T.P.Lacerda, 20 XII 1979.

Cynolebias affinis - MZUSP 36448, 1 paratype; MZUSP 36449, 1 paratype; Uruguay: Tacuarembó: Arroyo Tres Cruces flood plains; L.H.Amato, 3 XI 1985. MZUSP 36446, 1 paratype of *C. cyaneus*; MZUSP 36447, 1 paratype of *C. cyaneus*; Brazil: Rio Grande do Sul: Rio Pardo; L.R.Malabarba, C.A.Lucena & R.E.Reis, 12 IX 1983. - UFRJ 269, 12 ex.; Brazil: Rio Grande do Sul: Rio Pardo; G.C.Brasil, VIII 1988. - UFRJ 270, 11 ex.; UFRJ 271, 1(*); Brazil: Rio Grande do Sul: Cachoeira do Sul; G.C.Brasil, VIII 1988.

Cynolebias albipunctatus - MZUSP 41378, holotype; MZUSP 41379, 9 paratypes; UFRJ 160, 35 ex.; UFRJ 647, 2 ex. (*); Brazil: Bahia: Uauá; G.C.Brasil, 17 V 1989.

Cynolebias alexandri - MNRJ 11720, 4 ex.; MZUSP 37205, 2 ex.; MZUSP 38473, 2 ex. (*); Brazil: Rio Grande do Sul: Uruguaiana; U.Caramaschi, M.Soma & J.Jim, 19 VII 1980.

Cynolebias antenori - MNRJ 4542, 7 ex.; Brazil: Ceara: Russas; W.Franca & A.L.Carvalho, 3 VIII 1945. - MZUSP 38422, 1 ex. (*); aquarium material. - MZUSP 38342, 29 ex.; Brazil: Ceara: Paracajus; G.C.Brasil, IX 1972.

Cynolebias bellottii - MNRJ 9753, 3 ex.; Argentina: Buenos Aires: near La Plata; R. Lopez, R. Vaz-Ferreira, B. Soriano & J. Soriano, 3 XI 1962. - MNRJ 11350, 2 ex.; Argentina: Buenos Aires: Punta Lara; R.Vaz-Ferreira & B. Sierra, 2 XI 1962. - MZUSP 38416, 1 ex. (*); MZUSP 38412, 1 ex.; Uruguay; VI 1986.

Cynolebias boitonei - MNRJ 9012, holotype; MNRJ 9013/18, 6 paratypes; Brazil: Distrito Federal: Brasília; J.Boitonei, IV 1959. - MNRJ 11376, 3 ex.; same locality; II 1976. - MZUSP 38418, 1 ex. (*); same locality; M. Ribeiro, V 1986.

Cynolebias bokermanni - MNRJ 11167, holotype; MNRJ 11168, 16 paratypes; Brazil: Bahia: Ilhéus; W.C.A.Bokermann, XII 1971. - MNRJ 11721, 9 ex.; MZUSP 38432, 2 ex. (*); same locality; U.Caramaschi, H.R.Silva & L.Carcerelli, 10 III 1986.

Cynolebias carvalhoi - MNRJ 5759, holotype, male; MNRJ 5760, paratypes, 4 ex.; Brazil: Santa Catarina: Porto União near Rio Iguassú; A.L.Carvalho & G.S.Myers, 21-25 IV 1944.

Cynolebias cinereus - MNRJ uncatalog., 2 ex.; Uruguay: Colonia; R. Vaz-Ferreira & B. Soriano, IX 1959. - MZUSP 38504, 1 ex. (*); Uruguay; 1986.

Cynolebias constanciae - MZUSP 36295, 8 ex.; Brazil: Rio de Janeiro: Barra de São João; W.J.E.M.Costa, M.C.C.Pinna, M.T.C.Lacerda & K.Tanizaki, 6 VII 1985. - MZUSP 38345, 13 ex.; MZUSP, 38425, 1 ex. (*); Brazil: Rio de Janeiro: Barra de Sao Joao; W.J.E.M.Costa & A.Peixoto, 27 X 1984. - MZUSP 36300, 8 ex.; Brazil: Rio de Janeiro: Barra de São João; W.J.E.M.Costa, M.C.C.Pinna; M.T.C.Lacerda, 23 II 1985. - MZUSP 38337, 5 ex.; Brazil: Rio de Janeiro: Barra de São João; R.Lacorte & P.S.Santos, 2 VII 1978.

Cynolebias costai - MZUSP 38437, 2 ex. (*); MZUSP 38332, 10 ex.; MZUSP 41386, 5 ex.; Brazil: Goias: Aruana; W.J.E.M.Costa, K.Tanizaki & M.T.C.Lacerda, 29 I l986. - UFRJ 162, 2 ex.(*); UFRJ 163, 4 ex.; Brazil: Mato Grosso: Cocalinhos-Serra Dourada road;

G.C.Brasil, M.T.C.Lacerda, P.M.Araujo & G.Coelho, I 1988.

Cynolebias elongatus - MNRJ 11400, 2 ex.; Argentina: Buenos Aires: Punta Lara; R. Vaz-Ferreira & B. Sierra, 2 XI 1962.

Cynolebias flammeus - UFRJ 157, 33 ex.; Brazil: Goiás: Nova Roma; G.C.Brasil, D.Nielsen & M.T.C.Lacerda, 5 III 1989. - MNRJ 11552, holotype; MNRJ 11553, 3 paratypes; MCP 12795, 2 paratypes; UFRJ 159, 10 ex.; UFRJ 280, 1 ex.(*); Brazil: Tocantins: Rio Bezerra; W.J.E.M.Costa, 11 I 1989.

Cynolebias flavicaudatus - UFRJ 144, 23 ex.; Brazil: Minas Gerais: Januária; G.C.Brasil, 12 II 1990. - MZUSP 40129, holotype; MZUSP 40130, 3 paratypes; MNRJ 11556, 2 paratypes; MHNM 3252, 2 paratypes; UFRJ 146, 4 ex.; UFRJ 281, 1 ex.(*); Brazil: Pernambuco: Lagoa Grande; G.C.Brasil, 16 V 1989.

Cynolebias griseus - MZUSP 40119, holotype; MZUSP 40120, 3 paratypes; UFRJ 150, 2 ex.; UFRJ 319, 1 ex.; Brazil: Goiás: Nova Roma; G.C.Brasil, D.Nielsen & M.T.C.Lacerda, 5 III 1989.

Cynolebias gymnoventris - MZUSP 36450, 1 paratype; MZUSP 36451, 1 paratype; Uruguay: Rocha: Arroyo India Muerta flood plains; L.H.Amato, G.Dittricht & C.Pérez, 10 IX 1984.

Cynolebias magnificus - MZUSP 41374, holotype; MZUSP 41375, 8 paratypes; UFRJ 154, 12 ex.; UFRJ 260, 1 ex.(*); Brazil: Minas Gerais: Manga; G.C.Brasil, 10 II 1990.

Cynolebias microphthalmus - (see Systematic Section).

Cynolebias myersi - MNRJ 9849, holotype; MNRJ 9850, paratype; MNRJ 9851, paratypes; Brazil: Espírito Santo: Conceição da Barra; A.L.Carvalho, 9 VIII 1969. MZUSP 38336, 3 ex.; Brazil: Espirito Santo: Conceicao da Barra; V. Teixeira & J.C.Ghisolfi, 1986. - UFRJ 249, 31 ex.; UFRJ 282, 1 ex.(*); Brazil: Bahia: Mucuri; G.C.Brasil, IX 1989. - UFRJ 250, 12 ex.; Brazil: Bahia: Caravelas; G.C.Brasil, IX 1989. - UFRJ 377, 2 ex.; Brazil: Bahia: Mucuri; W.J.E.M.Costa, M.Melgaço, F.Pitanga & C.P.Bove. - MNRJ 10613, holotype of *C.*

izecksohni; MNRJ 10615, 2 paratypes of *C. izecksohni*; MZUSP 14721, paratype of *C. izecksohni*; Brazil: Espírito Santo: Linhares; C.A.G.Cruz, J.F.Pinheiro & S.P.C.Silva, 18 I 1980.

Cynolebias nigripinnis - MNRJ 9751, 4 ex.; Uruguay: Colonia: Hisneritos; R.Vaz-Ferreira & J.Soriano, VII 1963.

Cynolebias notatus - MZUSP 39985, holotype; MZUSP 39986, 3 paratypes; MNRJ 11559, 2 paratypes; MHNM 3251, 2 paratypes; UFRJ 155, 10 ex.; UFRJ 268, 1 ex.(*); Brazil: Goiás: Alvorada do Norte; G.C.Brasil, D.Nielsen & M.T.C.Lacerda, 4 III 1989.

Cynolebias perforatus - MZUSP 41376, holotype; MZUSP 41377, 3 paratypes; UFRJ 156, 1 ex.; Brazil: Minas Gerais: Januária; G.C.Brasil, 12 II 1990.

Cynolebias porosus - UFRJ 648, 10 ex.; Brazil: Bahia: Canudos; G.C.Brasil, 1988. - UFRJ 649, 18 ex.; UFRJ 650, 2 ex. (*); Brazil: Bahia: Euclides da Cunha; G.C.Brasil, 1988.

Cynolebias whitei - MNRJ 11399, 2 ex.; Brazil: Rio de Janeiro: São Pedro da Aldeia; L.E.M.Cardoso, W.D.Bandeira & G.A.Nunan, 1 VIII 1982. - MNRJ 11366, 28 ex.; Brazil: Rio de Janeiro: Cabo Frio; G.W.A. Nunan, II 1984. - MNRJ 11361, 7 ex.; Brazil: Rio de Janeiro: São Pedro da Aldeia; L.E.M.Cardoso, W.D.Bandeira & G.W.A.Nunan, 1 VIII 1982. - MNRJ 11398, 12 ex.; Brazil: Rio de Janeiro: São Pedro da Aldeia; A.L.Carvalho, no date. - MZUSP 38338, 16 ex.; MZUSP 38436, 1 ex. (*); Brazil: Rio de Janeiro: São Pedro da Aldeia; S.P.C.Silva, I 1984. - MZUSP 38387, 1 ex.; Brazil: Rio de Janeiro: Maricá; W.J.E.M.Costa, XI 1985. - MZUSP 38386, 19 ex.; Brazil: Rio de Janeiro: Maricá; W.J.E.M.Costa, K. Tanizaki & M.T.C.Lacerda, 5 X 1985. - MZUSP 38341, 63 ex.; Brazil: Rio de Janeiro: Barra de São João; W.J.E.M.Costa, K.Tanizaki & M.T.C.Lacerda, 14 XII 1985. - MZUSP 38340, 41 ex.; Brazil: Rio de Janeiro; W.J.E.M.Costa, K.Tanizaki & M.T.C.Lacerda, 14 XII 1985. - MZUSP 38413, 1 ex. (*); Brazil: Rio de Janeiro: Barra de São João; W.J.E.M.Costa,

1985.

Cynolebias wolterstorffi - MNRJ 11381, 8 ex.; Brazil: Rio Grande do Sul: Rio Grande; B.N.Barcelos, 4 X 1955. - MNRJ 11404, 2 ex.; Brazil: Rio Grande do Sul: Sao Leopoldo; T. Lacerda, 18 X 1967. - MZUSP 38421, 1 ex. (*); MZUSP 38348, 4 ex.; Brazil: Rio Grande do Sul: Porto Alegre; 1986. - MZUSP 38347, 2 ex.; Brazil: Rio Grande do Sul: Sao Leopoldo; W.Fries, R.Massman & R.P.Leal, 9 IX 1964.

Cynolebias viarius - MNRJ 9748, 2 ex.; Uruguay: Rocha: near Balneario Aguas Dulces; R. Vaz-Ferreira, B. Soriano & J. Soriano, 29 VII 1963.

Cynolebias zonatus - MZUSP 40131, holotype; MZUSP 40132, 1 paratype; MNRJ 2 paratypes; MHNM 3250, 1 paratype; UFRJ 142, 6 ex.; UFRJ 279, 1 ex.(*); Brazil: Minas Gerais: Unaí; G.C.Brasil, 3 III 1989.

Cynopoecilus melanotaenia - UFRJ 276, 8 ex.; Brazil: Santa Catarina: southern coastal plain; G.C.Brasil, VIII 1988. - MZUSP 38777, 11 ex.; MZUSP 38431, 2 ex. (*); Brazil: Rio Grande do Sul: Pelotas; Expedição Departamento de Zoologia, 22 VIII 1966.

Leptolebias aureoguttatus - UFRJ 172, 2 ex.(*); Aquarium material. - UFRJ 199, 7 ex.; Brazil: Paraná: Paranaguá; W.J.E.M.Costa, 21 XII 1985. - SU 36524, 10 ex.; idem; A.L.Carvalho & G.S.Myers, 1944. - CAGC 105, 3 ex.; idem; O.L.Peixoto, E. Izecksohn & C.A.G. Cruz, 10 V 1974. - CAGC 100, 7 ex.; Brazil: São Paulo: Registro; Sansão, Raimundo, Albuquerque, Izecksohn & Cruz, 16 X 1971. - CAGC 101, 8 ex.; idem; J.Silva, E.Izecksohn & C.A.G.Cruz, 3 XI 1972. CAGC 102, 5 ex.; idem; J.Silva, E.Izecksohn & C.A.G.Cruz, 3 XI 1973.

Leptolebias cruzi - MZUSP 36297, holotype; MZUSP 36298, 8 paratypes; MZUSP 36299, 8 paratypes; MNRJ 11290, 6 paratypes; MNRJ 11291, 2 paratypes; Brazil: Rio de Janeiro: Barra de São João; W.J.E.M. Costa, 1985. - MNRJ 11289, 3 paratypes; idem; L.E.M.Cardoso, 12 VII 1983. - CAGC 124, 14 paratypes; idem; E. Izecksohn &

C.A.G.Cruz, 1975. - UFRJ 173, 1 ex.(*); Brazil: Rio de Janeiro: Barra de São João; W.J.E.M.Costa & E.Vicente, 5 IX 1990.

Leptolebias fluminensis - UFRJ 175, 1 ex.(*); Aquarium material. - UFRJ 184, 2 ex.; Brazil: Rio de Janeiro: Maricá; W.J.E.M.Costa, 20 X 1990. - MNRJ 10621, holotype of *C. nanus*; MNRJ 10622, paratype of *C. nanus*; MZUSP 25229/30, 2 paratypes of *C. nanus*; Brazil: Rio de janeiro: Cava; C.A.G.Cruz, E.Izecksohn, M.C.A.Barbosa & O.L.Peixoto, VII 1979. - MZUSP 37199, holotype of *C. citrinipinnis*; MNRJ 11310, 3 paratypes; MZUSP 37198, 6 paratypes; Brazil: Rio de Janeiro: Maricá; K.Tanizaki & M.T.C.Lacerda, 14 VIII 1986. - MZUSP 37197, 3 paratypes of *C. citrinipinnis*; idem; K.Tanizaki, 9 VIII 1986. - SU 36522, 9 paratypes of *C. opalescens*; Brazil: Rio de Janeiro: Base of Serra de Petrópolis; T.White, 1 VI 1941. - MNRJ 11301, 3 ex.; idem; H.S.Lopez, I 1944. - CAGC 130, 1 ex.; Brazil: Rio de Janeiro; Itaguaí; M.T.C.Lacerda, 30 VIII 1983.

Leptolebias marmoratus - SU 36524, 10 paratypes of *C. zingiberinus*; Brazil: Rio de Janeiro: base of Serra de Petrópolis; T.White, 1941. - MNRJ 4739, 1 paratype of *C. sichelleri*; idem; G.Sicheller, 1938.

Leptolebias leitaoi - UFRJ 171, 1 ex.(*); Aquarium material.

Leptolebias minimus - SU 36526, 4 paratypes; Brazil: Rio de Janeiro: Itaguaí; T.White, 1941. - MZUSP 36296, 10 ex.; idem; W.J.E.M.Costa, 20 IV 1985. - SU 50193, paratype of *C. ladigesi*; H.Griem, 1955. - MZUSP 36423, holotype of *C. fractifasciatus*; MZUSP 36424, 11 paratypes of *C. fractifasciatus*; Brazil: Rio de Janeiro: Maricá; W.J.E.M.Costa, 1985- UFRJ 147, 5 ex.; idem; W.J.E.M.Costa & G.C.Brasil, 14 X 1989. UFRJ 174, 2 ex.(*); W.J.E.M.Costa & E.Vicente, 5 IX 1990. - UFRJ 185, 7 ex.; W.J.E.M.Costa, M.Melgaço & K.Tanizaki, 20 X 1990.

Leptolebias sandrii - SU 36528, 3 paratypes of *C. splendens*; Brazil: Rio de Janeiro: Base of Serra de Petrópolis:

T.White, VII-VIII 1941. - MNRJ 11302, 23 ex.; idem; G.S.Myers & P.M.Ribeiro, 14 I 1944. - MNRJ 11302, 1 ex.; idem; H.S.Lopez, I 1944. - MZUSP 38443, 2 ex. (*); MNRJ uncatalog., 6 ex.; Brazil: Rio de Janeiro: Magé; K.Tanizaki, 1986.

Maratecoara lacortei - MZUSP 41388, 1 ex.; MZUSP 41389, 4 ex.; MZUSP 41390, 3 ex.(*); UFRJ 275, 1 ex.; Brazil: Mato Grosso: Cocalinhos-Serra Dourada road; G.C.Brasil, M.T.C.Lacerda & P.M.Araujo, II 1988.

Millerichthys robustus - UMMZ 194706, 14 paratypes (4*); México: Vera Cruz: near Jesus Carranza; J.W. Atz & F.G. Wood, 4 III 1948.

Plesiolebias aruana - UFRJ 387, 15 ex.; Brazil: Goiás: Aruanã; W.J.E.M.Costa & K.Tanizaki, 28 I 1986.

Plesiolebias bellus - (see Systematic Section).

Plesiolebias damascenoi - MZUSP 41391, holotype; MZUSP 41392, 2 paratypes(*); MZUSP 41393, 1 paratype; Brazil: Mato Grosso: Poconé-Porto Cercado road; J.D.Soares, III 1990.

Plesiolebias glaucopterus - MZUSP 38533, holotype; MZUSP 38534, 1 paratype; MZUSP 38396, 2 paratypes; MNRJ 11406, 1 paratype; Brazil: Mato Grosso: Cáceres; P.D.Cardoso, 7 III 1987. - UFRJ 120, 2 ex.; Brazil: Mato Grosso: Poconé-Poto Cercado road; J.D.Soares, II 1990.

Plesiolebias lacerdai - MNRJ 11556, holotype; MNRJ 11557, 3 paratypes; MCP 12799, 2 paratypes; UFRJ 121, 2 ex.(*); UFRJ 164, 10 ex.; Brazil: Mato Grosso: Cocalinhos-Serra Dourada road; G.C.Brasil, M.T.C.Lacerda & P.M.Araujo, I 1988.

Plesiolebias xavantei - MZUSP 35418, holotype; MZUSP 35419, 10 paratypes; ZMA 119.416, 2 paratypes; MHNM 2490/1, 2 paratypes; MZUSP 38417, 4 ex.(*); Brazil: Tocantins: Porto Nacional; W.J.E.M.Costa, K.Tanizaki & M.T.C.Lacerda, 31 I 1986. - UFRJ 122, 1 ex.; Aquarium material.

Terranatos dolichopterus - MZUSP 37201, 1 ex.; MZUSP 38414, 2 ex.(*); Venezuela: Cojedes: between Tinaco and El Baúl; L.Aguana, 2 VII 1972

	MZUSP 42310 m	UFRJ 385 m	UFRJ 386 f	MZUSP 42311 f
SL (mm)	16.5	15.5	15.0	13.0
Body depth	25.2	24.8	23.7	22.7
Head length	30.3	31.0	29.4	29.2
Head depth	24.5	24.8	21.7	21.9
Head width	19.1	19.7	18.7	20.0
Eye diameter	34.0	34.4	35.2	35.5
Predorsal length	70.6	71.0	69.6	70.4
Prepelvic length	52.1	50.0	51.5	51.2
Depth of caudal peduncle	15.2	13.2	14.0	13.8
Length of dorsal fin base	12.7	12.3	12.7	12.7
Length of anal fin base	20.0	21.9	21.1	20.0
Dorsal rays	9	9	9	10
Anal rays	14	13	15	14
Scales in longitudinal series	27	27	26	27
Scales in transversal series	9	9	9	9
Horizontal scale rows around caudal peduncle	16	16	16	16

Table 1. Morphometric and meristic data of *Plesiolebias bellus*. Morphometric data are expressed in % SL, except eye diameter in % of head length; m : male, f: female.

Table 2. Morphometric and meristic data of *Cynolebias microphthalmus*. Morphometric data are expressed in % SL, except eye diameter in % of head length.

	MZUSP 38343	MZUSP 38343	MZUSP 42312	MZUSP 38343
SL (mm)	89.9	96.8	97.5	97.9
Body depth	33.2	34.0	33.8	33.9
Head length	31.8	32.2	30.1	30.7
Head depth	31.5	33.1	31.6	31.2
Head width	22.4	22.3	22.3	20.9
Eye diameter	16.6	15.4	17.2	16.6
Predorsal length	66.0	62.9	62.8	63.0
Prepelvic length	47.9	48.3	48.4	48.9
Depth of caudal peduncle	16.2	15.9	14.8	16.5
Length of dorsal fin base	26.9	27.7	26.8	26.7
Length of anal fin base	33.8	33.3	36.4	34.5
Dorsal rays	17	18	17	17
Anal rays	20	20	20	20
Scales in longitudinal series*	50	50	50	50
Scales in transversal series*	18	18	18	18
Horizontal scale rows around caudal peduncle*	30	30	30	30

* - approximate values in very irregular series.

	C. constanciae	L. cruzi
Filamentous algae	25	15
Rotifera	15	85
Branchiopoda	90	95
Copepoda	20	55
Ostracoda	75	70
Crustaceans (total)	90	100
Acarina	10	15
Chironomidae	65	35
Ephemeroptera	5	20
Aquatic immature stages of insects (total*)	90	50

* - Includes Chironomidae , Ephemeroptera, and unidentified larval forms.

Table 3. Frequency of food categories (%) found in stomach content analysis of *Cynolebias constanciae* and *Leptolebias cruzi*.

ADDENDUM

After the above went to press, some additional papers on Cynolebiatinae were published. The new names and systematic accounts are given below.

Cynolebias duraznensis Reichert

Cynolebias duraznensis Reichert, 1992:58. Nomen nudem.

Remarks. –Reichert (1992) cited the name *C. duraznensis* as an undescribed species from Uruguay, but does not present any diagnostic characters for it. Thus, according to the International Code of Zoological Nomenclature, this name is considered a *nomen nudem*. The two included illustrations of this species show a fish identical with *C. affinis*.

Cynolebias hellneri Berkenkamp

Cynolebias hellneri Berkenkamp, 1993:9. Original description; road Manga-Itacarambi, Minas Gerais, Brazil.
Cynolebias fulminantis Costa & Brasil, 1993:194. Original description; Guanambi, Bahia, Brazil.

Diagnosis.–This species is similar to *C. magnificus*. Males of the two species share a unique combination of characters: predorsal length short (42.8-47.3% SL), dorsal region of head red, no filamentous dorsal fin rays, and alternate red and dark blue bars present in anterodorsal region of body sides. It is distinguished from *C. magnificus* by the males having fewer dorsal fin rays (21-23 vs. 23-25), a subtruncate caudal fin (vs. rounded), a hyaline pectoral fin (vs. red), and paired fins with longitudinal blue lines (vs. transverse blue bars).
Description.–Dorsal and anal fins pointed in males, rounded in females. No filamentous rays in dorsal and anal fins. Caudal fin subtruncate in males, rounded in females. Pectoral fin elliptical. Tip of pectoral fin reaches base of seventh anal ray in males and base of second in females. Tip of pelvic fin reaches base of third anal fin ray in males and base of second in females. Dorsal fin origin opposite second anal fin ray in males and third in females. Dorsal fin rays 21(2) or 22(2) in males, 15(1), 16(2), or 17(1) in females. Anal fin rays 20(2), 21(1) or 22(1) in males, 18(1), 19(1), 20(1), or 21(1) in females. Caudal fin rays 20(1), 21(5), or 22(2). Pectoral fin rays 12(8). Pelvic fin rays 5(8). Scales in longitudinal series 27(8). Scales in transverse series 11(8). Horizontal scale rows around caudal peduncle 12(8). Neuromasts in supraorbital series 14(2) or 19(1). Neuromasts in infraorbital series 19(1), 23(1), or 24(1). Neuromasts in preopercular series 16(1), 17(1), or 20(1).
Coloration.–Male: Sides of body predominantly crimson, with a small, vertical brilliant blue streak on anterior region of each scale; three red bars on anterodorsal part of body alternating with dark blue bars. Belly pale orange. Scales of dorsal region of head red with blue centers. Opercular region pale greenish golden. Iris brown; eye with a black bar. Unpaired fins crimson to red, with longitudinal bright blue lines extending from the base to the fin edge, alternating with parallel, similar lines crossing only the distal half of the fin. Pectoral fin hyaline. Pelvic fin blue. Female: Sides of body pale purplish brown, with about 15 irregular gray dorsoventral bars, and a black spot centered on flank. Belly golden. Opercular region pale greenish golden. Iris brown; eye

crossed by a black bar. Fins hyaline.

Distribution.–Middle Rio Sao Francisco basin, Minas Gerais and Bahia, Brazil.

Cynolebias leptocephalus Costa & Brasil

Cynolebias leptocephalus Costa & Brasil, 1993:196. Original description; Guanambi, Bahia, Brazil.

Diagnosis.–Similar to *C. griseus, C. porosus, C. albinotatus,* and *C. perforatus,* with which it shares the following combination of characters: Frontal squamation consisting of about 20 irregularly distributed small scales; neuromasts in supraorbital series numerous (38-41); and dark blotches on posterodorsal region of head sides. *Cynolebias leptocephalus* is readily distinguished from these species by its deeply concave dorsal profile of the head, and dark bars on body sides (versus dark bars present only in juvenile stages). Males of *C. leptocephalus* also differ from males of these species in being more slender (body depth 23.3-28.5% SL vs. 30.5-35.1% SL; head depth 27.1-28.0% SL vs. 30.4-34.1% SL; depth of caudal peduncle 13.4-14.2% SL vs. 14.5-17.8% SL) and by having shorter dorsal and anal fin bases (length of dorsal fin base 24.3-25.3% SL vs. 26.0-29.7% SL; length of anal fin base 28.1-29.5% SL vs. 31.5-36.6% SL).

Description.–Dorsal and anal fins gently pointed. No filamentous rays in dorsal and anal fins. Caudal fin rounded. Pectoral fin rounded. Tip of pectoral fin reaches base of second anal fin ray in males and urogenital papilla in females. Tip of pelvic fin reaches base of third anal fin ray. Dorsal fin origin opposite fourth anal fin ray in males and fifth in females. Anterodorsal region of head with a deep concavity, more pronounced in males. Dorsal fin rays 17(1) or 19(1) in males, 17(2) in females. Anal fin rays 20(1) or 22(1) in males, 20(1) or 21(1) in females. Caudal fin rays 27(1), 29(2), or 30(1). Pectoral fin rays 13(1) or 15(3). Pelvic fin rays 5(4). Scales in longitudinal series 35(1), 38(1), or 42(1). Scales in transverse series 16(1) or 18(3). Horizontal scale rows around caudal peduncle 24(3) or 26(1). Neuromasts in supraorbital series 38(1) or 41(1). Neuromasts in infraorbital series 39(1) or 40(1). Neuromasts in preopercular series 35(1) or 39(1).

Coloration.–Male: Sides of body pale purplish brown, with about 15 dark gray dorsoventral bars and light blue dots scattered over dorsal and midlateral regions. Posterodorsal region of head sides and anterodorsal region of body golden with dark gray blotches. Sides of head purple. Iris brown, eye with a black bar. Unpaired fins dark blue with light blue dots. Paired fins hyaline. Female: Sides of body pale brown, with about 15 dark gray dorsoventral bars. Posterodorsal region of head sides and anterodorsal region of body sides pale brown with dark gray blotches. Sides of head pale purple. Iris brown; eye with a black bar. Fins hyaline.

Index

Page numbers in **bold face** refer to the main reference for the subject; page numbers in *italics* refer to photos of the subject; page numbers in normal type rfer to synonyms.